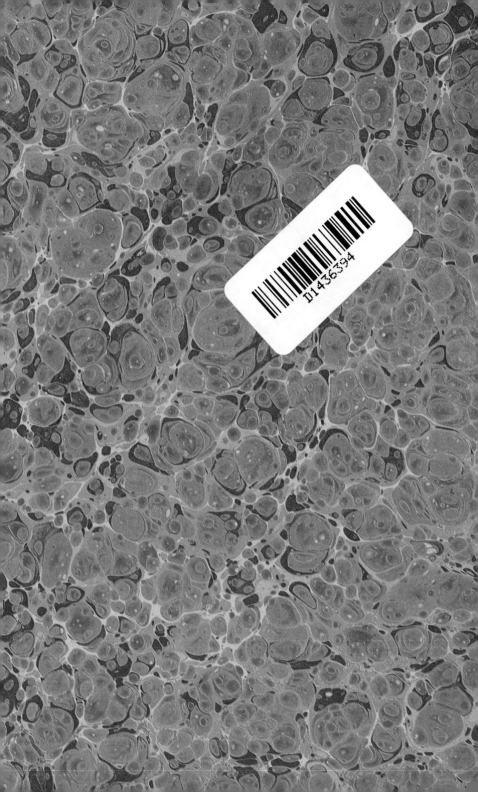

Reprinted 1983 from the 1849 edition.
Cover design © 1980 Time-Life Books Inc.
Library of Congress CIP data following page 312.

This volume is bound in leather.

LIFE

IN

THE FAR WEST

BY

GEORGE FREDERICK RUXTON

AUTHOR OF " TRAVELS IN MEXICO," &c.

WILLIAM BLACKWOOD AND SONS
EDINBURGH AND LONDON.
M.DCCC.XLIX.

ORIGINALLY PUBLISHED IN BLACKWOOD'S MAGAZINE.

JOHN HUGHES, PRINTER, EDINBURGH.

GEORGE FREDERICK RUXTON.

THE London newspapers of October 1848 contained the mournful tidings of the death, at St Louis on the Mississipi, and at the early age of twenty-eight, of Lieutenant George Frederick Ruxton, formerly of her Majesty's 89th regiment, the author of the following sketches.

Many men, even in the most enterprising periods of our history, have been made the subjects of elaborate biography, with far less title to the honour than this lamented young officer. Time was not granted him to embody in a permanent shape a tithe of his personal experiences and strange adventures in three quarters of the globe. Considering, indeed, the amount of physical labour he underwent, and the extent of the fields over which his wanderings spread, it is almost surprising he found leisure to write so much. At the early age of seventeen, Mr Ruxton quitted Sandhurst, to learn the practical part of a soldier's profession in the civil wars of Spain. He obtained a commission in a squadron of lancers then attached to the division of General Diego Leon, and was actively engaged in several of the most important combats of the campaign. For his marked gallantry on these occasions, he received from Queen Isabella II., the cross of the first class of the order of St Fernando, an honour which has seldom been awarded to one so young. On his return from Spain he found himself gazetted to a commission in the 89th regiment; and it was whilst serving with that distinguished corps in Canada that he first became acquainted with the stirring scenes of Indian life, which he has since so graphically portrayed. His eager and enthusiastic spirit soon became wearied with the monotony of the barrack-room; and, yielding to that impulse which in him was irresistibly developed, he resigned his commission, and directed his steps towards the stupendous wilds, tenanted only by the red Indian, or by the solitary American trapper.

Those familiar with Mr Ruxton's writings cannot fail to have remarked the singular delight with

which he dwells upon the recollections of this portion of his career, and the longing which he carried
with him, to the hour of his death, for a return to
those scenes of primitive freedom. "Although
liable to an accusation of barbarism," he writes, " I
must confess that the very happiest moments of my
life have been spent in the wilderness of the Far
West; and I never recall, but with pleasure, the
remembrance of my solitary camp in the Bayou
Salade, with no friend near me more faithful than
my rifle, and no companions more sociable than my
good horse and mules, or the attendant cayute
which nightly serenaded us. With a plentiful
supply of dry pine-logs on the fire, and its cheerful
blaze streaming far up into the sky, illuminating
the valley far and near, and exhibiting the animals,
with well-filled bellies, standing contentedly at rest
over their picket-fire, I would sit cross-legged,
enjoying the genial warmth, and, pipe in mouth,
watch the blue smoke as it curled upwards, building
castles in its vapoury wreaths, and, in the fantastic
shapes it assumed, peopling the solitude with
figures of those far away. Scarcely, however, did
I ever wish to change such hours of freedom for all
the luxuries of civilised life; and, unnatural and

extraordinary as it may appear, yet such is the fascination of the life of the mountain hunter, that I believe not one instance could be adduced of even the most polished and civilised of men, who had once tasted the sweets of its attendant liberty, and freedom from every worldly care, not regretting the moment when he exchanged it for the monotonous life of the settlements, nor sighing and sighing again once more to partake of its pleasures and allurements."

On his return to Europe from the Far West, Mr Ruxton, animated with a spirit as enterprising and fearless as that of Raleigh, planned a scheme for the exploration of Central Africa, which was thus characterised by the president of the Royal Geographical Society, in his anniversary address for 1845 : —" To my great surprise, I recently conversed with an ardent and accomplished youth, Lieutenant Ruxton, late of the 89th regiment, who had formed the daring project of traversing Africa in the parallel of the southern tropic, and has actually started for this purpose. Preparing himself by previous excursions on foot, in North Africa and Algeria, he sailed from Liverpool early in December last, in the Royalist, for Ichaboe. From that spot he was to

repair to Walvish Bay, where we have already
mercantile establishments. The intrepid traveller
had received from the agents of these establishments
such favourable accounts of the nations towards the
interior, as also of the nature of the climate, that
he has the most sanguine hopes of being able to
penetrate to the central region, if not of traversing
it to the Portuguese colonies of Mozambique. If
this be accomplished, then indeed will Lieutenant
Ruxton have acquired for himself a permanent name
among British travellers, by making us acquainted
with the nature of the axis of the great continent
of which we possess the southern extremity."

In pursuance of this hazardous scheme, Ruxton,
with a single companion, landed on the coast of
Africa, a little to the south of Ichaboe, and commenced his journey of exploration. But it seemed
as if both nature and man had combined to baffle
the execution of his design. The course of their
travel lay along a desert of moving sand, where no
water was to be found, and little herbage, save a
coarse tufted grass, and twigs of the resinous myrrh.
The immediate place of their destination was Angra
Peguena, on the coast, described as a frequented
station, but which in reality was deserted. One

ship only was in the offing when the travellers arrived, and, to their inexpressible mortification, they discovered that she was outward bound. No trace was visible of the river or streams laid down in the maps as falling into the sea at this point, and no resource was left to the travellers save that of retracing their steps—a labour for which their strength was hardly adequate. But for the opportune assistance of a body of natives, who encountered them at the very moment when they were sinking from fatigue and thirst, Ruxton and his companion would have been added to the long catalogue of those whose lives have been sacrificed in the attempt to explore the interior of that fatal country.

The jealousy of the traders, and of the missionaries settled on the African coast, who constantly withheld or perverted that information which was absolutely necessary for the successful prosecution of the journey, induced Ruxton to abandon the attempt for the present. He made, however, several interesting excursions towards the interior, and more especially in the country of the Bosjesmans.

Finding his own resources inadequate for the accomplishment of his favourite project, Mr Ruxton, on his return to England, made application for Government assistance. But though this demand was not altogether refused, it having been referred to the Council of the Royal Geographical Society, and favourably reported upon by that body, so many delays interposed that Ruxton, in disgust, resolved to withdraw from the scheme, and to abandon that field of African research which he had already contemplated from its borders. He next bent his steps to Mexico; and, fortunately, has presented to the world his reminiscences of that country, in one of the most fascinating volumes which, of late years, has issued from the press. It would, however, appear that the African scheme, the darling project of his life, had again recurred to him at a later period; for, in the course of the present spring, before setting out on that journey which was destined to be his last, the following expressions occur in one of his letters :—

" My movements are uncertain, for I am trying to get up a yacht voyage to Borneo and the Indian Archipelago ; have volunteered to Government to explore Central Africa; and the Aborigines Protection Society wish me to go out to Canada to orga-

b

nise the Indian tribes; whilst, for my own part and
inclination, I wish to go to all parts of the world at
once."

As regards the volume to which this notice serves
as Preface, the editor does not hesitate to express a
very high opinion of its merits. Written by a man
untrained to literature, and whose life, from boy-
hood upwards, was passed in the field and on the
road, in military adventure and travel, its style is
yet often as remarkable for graphic terseness and
vigour, as its substance every where is for great
novelty and originality. The narrative of "Life in
the Far West" was first offered for insertion in
Blackwood's Magazine in the spring of 1848, when
the greater portion of the manuscript was sent, and
the remainder shortly followed. During its publi-
cation in that periodical, the wildness of the adventures related excited suspicions in certain quarters
as to their actual truth and fidelity. It may interest the reader to know that the scenes described
are pictures from life, the results of the author's
personal experience. The following are extracts
from letters addressed by him, in the course of last

summer, to the conductors of the Magazine above named :—

" I have brought out a few more softening traits in the characters of the mountaineers—but not at the sacrifice of truth—for some of them have their good points; which, as they are rarely allowed to rise to the surface, must be laid hold of at once before they sink again. Killbuck—that ' old hos ' *par exemple*, was really pretty much of a gentleman, as was La Bonté. Bill Williams, another ' hard case,' and Rube Herring, were ' some ' too.

" The scene where La Bonté joins the Chase family is so far true, that he did make a sudden appearance ; but, in reality, a day before the Indian attack. The Chases (and I wish I had not given the proper name *) did start for the Platte alone, and were stampedoed upon the waters of the Platte.

" The Mexican fandango *is true to the letter*.

---

* In accordance with this suggestion, the name was changed to Brand. The mountaineers, it seems, are more sensitive to type than to tomahawks ; and poor Ruxton, who always contemplated another expedition among them, would sometimes jestingly speculate upon his reception, should they learn that he had shown them up in print.

It does seem difficult to understand how they contrived to keep their knives out of the hump-ribs of
the mountaineers; but how can you account for
the fact, that, the other day, 4000 Mexicans, with
13 pieces of artillery, behind strong entrenchments
and two lines of parapets, were routed by 900 raw
Missourians; 300 killed, as many more wounded,
all their artillery captured, as well as several hundred prisoners; and that not one American was
killed in the affair? *This is positive fact.*

" I myself, with three trappers, cleared a fandango at Taos, armed only with bowie-knives—
some score Mexicans, at least, being in the room.

" With regard to the incidents of Indian attacks,
starvation, cannibalism, &c., I have invented not
one out of my own head. They are all matters of
history in the mountains; but I have, no doubt,
jumbled the *dramatis personæ* one with another,
and may have committed anachronisms in the
order of their occurrence."

Again he wrote as follows :—

" I think it would be as well to correct a misap-
prehension as to the truth or fiction of the paper.

It is no *fiction*. There is no incident in it which has not actually occurred, nor one character who is not well known in the Rocky Mountains, with the exception of two whose names are changed—the originals of these being, however, equally well known with the others."

His last letter, written just before his departure from England, a few weeks previously to his death, will hardly be read by any one who ever knew the writer, without a tear of sympathy for the sad fate of this fine young man, dying miserably in a strange land, before he had well commenced the hazardous journey whose excitement and dangers he so joyously anticipated :—

" As you say, human nature can't go on feeding on civilised fixings in this ' big village ;' and this child has felt like going West for many a month, being half froze for buffler meat and mountain doins. My route takes me *viâ* New York, the Lakes, and St Louis, to Fort Leavenworth, or Independence on the Indian frontier. Thence packing my ' possibles ' on a mule, and mounting a buffalo horse (Panchito, if he is alive), I strike the

Santa Fé trail to the Arkansa, away up that river
to the mountains, winter in the Bayou Salade,
where Killbuck and La Bonté joined the Yutes,
cross the mountains next spring to Great Salt
Lake—and that's far enough to look forward to—
always supposing my hair is not lifted by Comanche or Pawnee on the scalping route of the Coon
Creeks and Pawnee Fork."

Poor fellow! he spoke lightly, in the buoyancy
of youth and a confident spirit, of the fate he little
thought to meet, but which too surely overtook
him—not indeed by Indian blade, but by the no
less deadly stroke of disease. Another motive,
besides that love of rambling and adventure, which,
once conceived and indulged, is so difficult to eradi-
cate, impelled him across the Atlantic. He had for
some time been out of health at intervals, and he
thought the air of his beloved prairies would be
efficacious to work a cure. In a letter to a friend,
in the month of May last, he thus referred to the
probable origin of the evil:—

" I have been confined to my room for many
days, from the effects of an accident I met with in

the Rocky Mountains, having been spilt from the
bare back of a mule, and falling on the sharp picket
of an Indian lodge on the small of my back. I fear
I injured my spine, for I have never felt altogether
the thing since, and shortly after I saw you, the
symptoms became rather ugly. However, I am now
getting round again."

His medical advisers shared his opinion that he
had sustained internal injury from this ugly fall;
and it is not improbable that it was the remote,
but real cause of his dissolution. From whatsoever
this ensued, it will be a source of deep and lasting
regret to all who ever enjoyed opportunities of
appreciating the high and sterling qualities of
George Frederick Ruxton. Few men, so prepos-
sessing on first acquaintance, gained so much by
being better known. With great natural abilities
and the most dauntless bravery, he united a modesty
and gentleness peculiarly pleasing. Had he lived,
and resisted his friends' repeated solicitations to
abandon a roving life, and settle down in England,
there can be little doubt that he would have made
his name eminent on the list of those daring and
persevering men, whose travels in distant and dan-

gerous lands have accumulated for England, and
for the world, so rich a store of scientific and general information. And, although the few words it
has been thought right and becoming here to devote
to his memory, will doubtless be more particularly
welcome to his personal friends, we are persuaded
that none will peruse without interest this brief tri-
bute to the merits of a gallant soldier, and accomplished English gentleman.

LIFE IN THE FAR WEST.

CHAPTER I.

Away to the head waters of the Platte, where several small streams run into the south fork of that river, and head in the broken ridges of the "Divide" which separates the valleys of the Platte and Arkansa, were camped a band of trappers on a creek called Bijou. It was the month of October, when the early frosts of the coming winter had crisped and dyed with sober brown the leaves of the cherry and quaking ash belting the brooks; and the ridges and peaks of the Rocky Mountains were already covered with a glittering mantle of snow, sparkling in the still powerful rays of the autumn sun.

The camp had all the appearance of permanency; for not only did it comprise one or two unusually comfortable shanties, but the numerous stages on which huge stripes of buffalo meat were hanging in

A

process of cure, showed that the party had settled themselves here in order to lay in a store of provisions, or, as it is termed in the language of the mountains, " to make meat." Round the camp fed twelve or fifteen mules and horses, their forelegs confined by hobbles of raw hide; and, guarding these animals, two men paced backwards and forwards, driving in the stragglers, ascending ever and anon the bluffs which overhung the river, and leaning on their long rifles, whilst they swept with their eyes the surrounding prairie. Three or four fires burned in the encampment, at some of which Indian women carefully tended sundry steaming pots; whilst round one, which was in the centre of it, four or five stalwart hunters, clad in buckskin, sat cross-legged, pipe in mouth.

They were a trapping party from the north fork of Platte, on their way to wintering-ground in the more southern valley of the Arkansa; some, indeed, meditating a more extended trip, even to the distant settlements of New Mexico, the paradise of mountaineers. The elder of the company was a tall gaunt man, with a face browned by twenty years' exposure to the extreme climate of the mountains; his long black hair, as yet scarcely tinged with grey, hanging almost to his shoulders, but his cheeks and chin clean shaven, after the fashion of the mountain men. His dress was the usual hunting-frock of buckskin, with long fringes down the seams, with pantaloons similarly ornamented, and

moccasins of Indian make. Whilst his companions
puffed their pipes in silence, he narrated a few of
his former experiences of western life; and whilst
the buffalo " hump-ribs " and " tender loin " are
singing away in the pot, preparing for the hunters'
supper, we will note down the yarn as it spins from
his lips, giving it in the language spoken in the
" far west : "—

" 'Twas about ' calf-time,' maybe a little later,
and not a hunderd year ago, by a long chalk, that
the biggest kind of rendezvous was held ' to ' Independence, a mighty handsome little location away
up on old Missoura. A pretty smart lot of boys
was camp'd thar, about a quarter from the town,
and the way the whisky flowed that time was
' some ' now, _I_ can tell you. Thar was old Sam
Owins—him as got ' rubbed out ' * by the Spaniards at Sacramenty, or Chihuahuy, this hos doesn't
know which, but he ' went under ' † any how. Well,
Sam had his train along, ready to hitch up for the
Mexican country—twenty thunderin big Pittsburg
waggons ; and the way _his_ Santa Fé boys took in
the liquor beat all—eh, Bill ?"

" _Well_, it did."

" Bill Bent—his boys camped the other side the
trail, and they was all mountain men, wagh !—and
Bill Williams, and Bill Tharpe (the Pawnees took
his hair on Pawnee Fork last spring) : three Bills,

* Killed, ⎱ both terms adapted from the Indian figurative
† Died, ⎰ language.

and them three's all ' gone under.' Surely Hatcher
went out that time; and wasn't Bill Garey along,
too? Didn't him and Chabonard sit in camp for
twenty hours at a deck of Euker? Them was
Bent's Indian traders up on Arkansa. Poor Bill
Bent! them Spaniards made meat of him. He lost
his topknot to Taos. A ' clever' man was Bill
Bent as *I* ever know'd trade a robe or ' throw' a
bufler in his tracks. Old St Vrain could knock the
hind-sight off him though, when it came to shootin,
and old silver heels spoke true, she did: ' plum-
center' she was, eh?"

" *Well*, she wasn't nothin else."

" The Greasers * payed for Bent's scalp, they
tell me. Old St Vrain went out of Santa Fé with
a company of mountain men, and the way they
made 'em sing out was ' slick as shootin'. He
' counted a coup,' did St Vrain. He throwed a
Pueblo as had on poor Bent's shirt. I guess he
tickled that niggur's hump-ribs. Fort William †
aint the lodge it was, an' never will be agin, now
he's gone under; but St Vrain's ' pretty much of
a gentleman,' too; if he aint, I'll be dog-gone, eh,
Bill?"

" He is *so-o*."

" Chavez had his waggons along. He was only
a Spaniard any how, and some of his teamsters

* The Mexicans are called " Spaniards " or " Greasers " (from
heir greasy appearance) by the Western people.
† Bent's Indian trading fort on the Arkansa.

put a ball into him his next trip, and made a raise
of *his* dollars, wagh! Uncle Sam hung 'em for it,
I heard, but can't b'lieve it, nohow. If them
Spaniards wasn't born for shootin', why was beaver
made? You was with us that spree, Jemmy?"

"No *sirre-e*; I went out when Spiers lost his
animals on Cimmaron : a hunderd and forty mules
and oxen was froze that night, wagh!"

"Surely Black Harris was thar; and the darndest liar was Black Harris—for lies tumbled out of
his mouth like boudins out of a bufler's stomach.
He was the child as saw the putrefied forest in the
Black Hills. Black Harris come in from Laramie;
he'd been trapping three year an' more on Platte
and the ' other side ;' and, when he got into
Liberty, he fixed himself right off like a Saint
Louiy dandy. Well, he sat to dinner one day in
the tavern, and a lady says to him :—

" ' Well, Mister Harris, I hear you're a great
travler.'

" ' Travler, marm,' says Black Harris, ' this
niggur's no travler ; I ar' a trapper, marm, a moun-
tain-man, wagh !'

" ' Well, Mister Harris, trappers are great trav-
lers, and you goes over a sight of ground in your
perishinations, I'll be bound to say.'

" ' A sight, marm, this coon's gone over, if that's
the way your ' stick floats.'* I've trapped beaver

* Meaning—if that's what you mean. The " stick " is
tied to the beaver trap by a string ; and, floating on the

on Platte and Arkansa, and away up on Missoura
and Yaller Stone; I've trapped on Columbia, on
Lewis Fork, and Green River; I've trapped, marm,
on Grand River and the Heely (Gila). I've fout
the 'Blackfoot' (and d——d bad Injuns they ar);
I've 'raised the hair'* of more *than one* Apach,
and made a Rapaho 'come' afore now; I've trapped in heav'n, in airth, and h—; and scalp my old
head, marm, but I've seen a putrefied forest.'

" ' La, Mister Harris, a what ?'

" ' A putrefied forest, marm, as sure as my rifle's
got hind-sights, and *she* shoots center. I was out
on the Black Hills, Bill Sublette knows the time—
the year it rained fire—and every body knows
when that was. If thar wasn't cold doins about
that time, this child wouldn't say so. The snow
was about fifty foot deep, and the bufler lay dead
on the ground like bees after a beein'; not whar
we was tho', for *thar* was no bufler, and no meat,
and me and my band had been livin' on our mocas-
sins (leastwise the parflesh †), for six weeks; and
poor doins that feedin' is, marm, as you'll never
know. One day we crossed a 'cañon' and over a
'divide,' and got into a peraira, whar was green
grass, and green trees, and green leaves on the
trees, and birds singing in the green leaves, and

water, points out its position, should a beaver have carried
it away.
    * Scalped.
    † Soles made of buffalo hide.

this in Febrary, wagh! Our animals was like to
die when they see the green grass, and we all sung
out, ' hurraw for summer doins.'

" ' Hyar goes for meat,' says I, and I jest ups
old Ginger at one of them singing birds, and down
come the crittur elegant; its darned head spinning
away from the body, but never stops singing, and
when I takes up the meat, I finds it stone, wagh!
' Hyar's damp powder and no fire to dry it,' I says,
quite skeared.

" ' Fire be dogged,' says old Rube. ' Hyar's a
hos as 'll make fire come ;' and with that he takes
his axe and lets drive at a cotton wood. Schr-u-k
—goes the axe agin the tree, and out comes a bit
of the blade as big as my hand. We looks at the
animals, and thar they stood shaking over the grass,
which I'm dog-gone if it wasn't stone, too. Young
Sublette comes up, and he'd been clerking down to
the fort on Platte, so he know'd something. He
looks and looks, and scrapes the trees with his
butcher knife, and snaps the grass like pipe stems,
and breaks the leaves a-snappin' like Californy
shells.'

" ' What's all this, boy ?' I asks.

" ' Putrefactions,' says he, looking smart, ' putrefactions, or I'm a niggur.'

" ' La, Mister Harris,' says the lady, ' putrefactions! why, did the leaves, and the trees, and the
grass smell badly ?'

" ' Smell badly, marm!' says Black Harris, ' would

a skunk stink if he was froze to stone ? No, marm, this child didn't know what putrefaction was, and young Sublette's varsion wouldn't ' shine' nohow, so I chips a piece out of a tree and puts it in my trap-sack, and carries it in safe to Laramie. Well, old Captain Stewart, (a clever man was that, though he was an Englishman), he comes along next spring, and a Dutch doctor chap was along too. I shows him the piece I chipped out of the tree, and he called it a putrefaction too ; and so, marm, if that wasn't a putrefied peraira, what was it ? For this hos doesn't know, and *he* knows ' fat cow' from ' poor bull,' anyhow.'

" Well, old Black Harris is gone under too, I believe. He went to the ' Parks' trapping with a Vide Pôche Frenchman, who shot him for his bacca and traps. Darn them Frenchmen, they're no account any way you lays your sight. (Any bacca in your bag, Bill ? this beaver feels like chawing.)

" Well, any how, thar was the camp, and they was goin to put out the next morning ; and the last as come out of Independence was that ar English-man. He'd a nor-west* capote on, and a two-shoot gun rifled. Well, them English are darned fools ; they can't fix a rifle any ways ; but that one did shoot ' some ;' leastwise *he* made it throw plum-cen-

---

* The Hudson Bay Company having amalgamated with the American North West Company, is known by the name 'North West' to the southern trappers. Their employés usually wear Canadian capotes.

ter. He made the bufler ' come,' *he* did, and fout
well at Pawnee Fork too. What was his name?
All the boys called him Cap'en, and he got his fixings from old Choteau; but what he wanted out
thar in the mountains, I never jest rightly know'd.
He was no trader, nor a trapper, and flung about
his dollars right smart. Thar was old grit in him,
too, and a hair of the black b'ar at that.* They
say he took the bark off the Shians when he cleared
out of the village with old Beaver Tail's squaw.
He'd been on Yaller Stone afore that: Leclerc
know'd him in the Blackfoot, and up in the Chip-
peway country; and he had the best powder as
ever I flashed through life, and his gun was handsome, that's a fact. Them thar locks was grand;
and old Jake Hawken's nephey, (him as trapped on
Heeley that time), told me, the other day, as he
saw an English gun on Arkansa last winter as beat
all off hand.

" Nigh upon two hundred dollars I had in my
possibles, when I went to that camp to see the boys
afore they put out; and you know, Bill, as I sat to
' Euker' and ' seven up'† till every cent was gone.

" ' Take back twenty, old coon,' says Big John.

" ' H—'s full of such takes back,' says I; and I
puts back to town and fetches the rifle and the old
mule, puts my traps into the sack, gets credit for a

* A spice of the devil.
† "Euker," "poker," and "seven up," are the fashionable
games of cards.

couple of pounds of powder at Owin's store, and hyar I ar on Bijou, with half a pack of beaver, and running meat yet, old hos: so put a log on, and let's have a smoke.

"Hurraw, Jake, old coon, bear a hand, and let the squaw put them tails in the pot; for sun's down, and we'll have to put out pretty early to reach 'Black Tail' by this time to-morrow. Who's fust guard, boys? them cussed 'Rapahos' will be after the animals to-night, or I'm no judge of Injun sign. How many did you see, Maurice?"

"Enfant de Gârce, me see bout honderd, when I pass Squirrel Creek, one dam war-party, parceque, they no hosses, and have de lariats for steal des animaux. May be de Yutas in Bayou Salade."

"We'll be having trouble to-night, I'm thinking, if the devils are about. Whose band was it, Maurice?"

"Slim-Face—I see him ver close—is out; mais I think it White Wolf's."

"White Wolf, maybe, will lose his hair if he and his band knock round here too often. That Injun put me afoot when we was out on 'Sandy' that fall. This niggur owes him one, any how."

"H—'s full of White Wolves: go ahead, and roll out some of your doins across the plains that time."

"You seed sights that spree, eh, boy?"

"*Well*, we did. Some of em got their flints fixed this side of Pawnee Fork, and a heap of mule-

meat went wolfing. Just by Little Arkansa we saw
the first Injun. Me and young Somes was ahead
for meat, and I had hobbled the old mule and was
' approaching' some goats,* when I see the critturs
turn back their heads and jump right away for me.
' Hurraw, Dick!' I shouts, ' hyars brown-skin
acomin,' and off I makes for the mule. The young
greenhorn sees the goats runnin up to him, and not
being up to Injun ways, blazes at the first and
knocks him over. Jest then seven darned red
heads top the bluff, and seven Pawnees come
a-screechin upon us. I cuts the hobbles and jumps
on the mule, and, when I looks back, there was
Dick Somes ramming a ball down his gun like mad,
and the Injuns flinging their arrows at him pretty
smart, I tell you. ' Hurraw, Dick, mind your hair,'
and I ups old Greaser and let one Injun ' have it,'
as was going plum into the boy with his lance. *He*
turned on his back handsome, and Dick gets the
ball down at last, blazes away, and drops another.
Then we charged on em, and they clears off like
runnin cows; and I takes the hair off the heads of
the two we made meat of; and I do b'lieve thar's
some of them scalps on my old leggings yet.

" Well, Dick was as full of arrows as a porky-
pine: one was sticking right through his cheek,
one in his meat-bag, and two more 'bout his hump-
ribs. I tuk 'em all out slick, and away we go to

* Antelope are frequently called "goats" by the mountaineers.

camp, (for they was jost a-campin' when we went ahead) and carryin' the goat too. Thar' was a hurroo when we rode in with the scalps at the end of our guns. ' Injuns! Injuns!' was the cry from the greenhorns; ' we'll be 'tacked to-night, that's certain.'

" ' 'Tacked be ——— ' says old Bill; ' aint we men too, and white at that? Look to your guns, boys; send out a strong hos'-guard with the animals, and keep your eyes skinned.'

" Well, as soon as the animals were unhitched from the waggons, the guvner sends out a strong guard, seven boys, and old hands at that. It was pretty nigh upon sundown, and Bill had just sung out to ' corral.' The boys were drivin' in the animals, and we were all standin' round to get 'em in slick, when, ' howgh-owgh-owgh-owgh,' we hears right behind the bluff, and 'bout a minute and a perfect crowd of Injuns gallops down upon the animals. Wagh! war'nt thar hoopin'! We jump for the guns, but before we get to the fires, the Injuns were among the cavayard. I saw Ned Collyer and his brother, who were in the hos'-guard, let drive at 'em; but twenty Pawnees were round 'em before the smoke cleared from their rifles, and when the crowd broke the two boys were on the ground, and their hair gone. Well, that ar Englishman just saved the cavayard. He had his horse, a regular buffalo-runner, picketed round the fire quite handy, and as soon as he sees the fix, he jumps upon her and rides right into the thick of the mules, and passes through 'em, firing his two-shoot gun at the Injuns, and, by Gor, he made two come. The mules, which was a snortin' with funk and running before the Injuns, as soon as they see the Englisman's mare (mules 'ill go to h— after a horse, you all know), followed her right into the corral, and thar they was safe. Fifty Pawnees come screechin' after 'em, but we was ready that time, and the way we throw'd 'em was something handsome, I tell you. But three of the hos'-guard got skeared—leastwise their mules did, and carried 'em off into the peraira, and the Injuns having enough of *us*, dashed after 'em right away. Them poor devils looked back miserable now, with about a hundred red varmints tearin' after their hair, and whooping like mad. Young Jem Bulcher was the last; and when he seed it was no use, and his time was nigh, he throw'd himself off the mule, and standing as upright as a hickory wiping stick, he waves his hand to us, and blazes away at the first Injun as come up, and dropped him slick; but the moment after, you may guess, *he* died.

" We could do nothin', for, before our guns were loaded, all three were dead and their scalps gone. Five of our boys got rubbed out that time, and seven Injuns lay wolf's meat, while a many more went away .gut-shot, I'll lay. How'sever, five of us went under, and the Pawnees made a raise of a dozen mules, wagh!"

Thus far, in his own words, we have accompanied the old hunter in his tale; and probably he would have taken us, by the time that the Squaw Chilipat had pronounced the beaver tails cooked, safely across the grand prairies—fording Cotton Wood, Turkey Creek, Little Arkansa, Walnut Creek, and Pawnee Fork—passed the fireless route of the Coon Creeks, through a sea of fat buffalo meat, without fuel to cook it; have struck the big river, and, leaving at the " Crossing" the waggons destined for Santa Fé, have trailed us up the Arkansa to Bent's Fort; thence up Boiling Spring, across the divide over to the southern fork of the Platte, away up to the Black Hills, and finally camped us, with hair still preserved, in the beaver-abounding valleys of the Sweet Water, and Câche la Poudre, under the rugged shadow of the Wind River mountains; if it had not so happened, at this juncture, as all our mountaineers sat cross-legged round the fire, pipe in mouth, and with Indian gravity listened to the yarn of the old trapper, interrupting him only with an occasional wagh! or with the exclamations of some participator in the events then under narration, who would every now and then put in a corroborative,—" This child remembers that fix," or, " hyar's a niggur lifted hair that spree," &c.— that a whizzing noise was heard in the air, followed by a sharp but suppressed cry from one of the hunters.

In an instant the mountaineers had sprung from

their seats, and, seizing the ever-ready rifle, each one had thrown himself on the ground a few paces beyond the light of the fire (for it was now nightfall;) but not a word escaped them, as, lying close, with their keen eyes directed towards the gloom of the thicket, near which the camp was placed, with rifles cocked, they waited a renewal of the attack. Presently the leader of the band, no other than Killbuck, who had so lately been recounting some of his experiences across the plains, and than whom no more crafty woodsman or more expert trapper ever tracked a deer or grained a beaverskin, raised his tall, leather-clad form, and, placing his hand over his mouth, made the prairie ring with the wild protracted note of an Indian war-whoop. This was instantly repeated from the direction where the animals belonging to the camp were grazing, under the charge of the horse-guard. Three shrill whoops answered the warning of the leader, and showed that the guard was on the alert, and understood the signal. However, with the manifestation of their presence, the Indians appeared to be satisfied; or, what is more probable, the act of aggression had been committed by some daring young warrior, who, being out on his first expedition, desired to strike the first *coup*, and thus signalise himself at the outset of the campaign. After waiting some few minutes, expecting a renewal of the attack, the mountaineers in a body rose from the ground and made towards the animals, with which they pre-

sently returned to the camp; and, after carefully
hobbling and securing them to pickets firmly driven
into the ground, mounting an additional guard, and
examining the neighbouring thicket, they once more
assembled round the fire, relit their pipes, and puffed
away the cheering weed as composedly as if no such
being as a Redskin, thirsting for their lives, was
within a thousand miles of their perilous encampment.

" If ever thar was bad Injuns on these plains,"
at last growled Killbuck, biting hard the pipe-stem
between his teeth, " it's these Rapahos, and the
meanest kind at that."

" Can't beat the Blackfeet, any how," chimed in
one La Bonté, from the Yellow Stone country, a
fine handsome specimen of a mountaineer. " However, one of you quit this arrow out of my hump,"
he continued, bending forwards to the fire, and
exhibiting an arrow sticking out under his right
shoulder-blade, and a stream of blood trickling
down his buckskin coat from the wound

This his nearest neighbour essayed to do; but
finding, after a tug, that it " would not come,"
expressed his opinion that the offending weapon
would have to be " butchered" out.   This was
accordingly effected with the ready blade of a scalp-
knife; and a handful of beaver-fur being placed on
the wound, and secured by a strap of buckskin
round the body, the wounded man donned his hunting-shirt once more, and coolly set about lighting

his pipe, his rifle lying across his lap, cocked and ready for use.

It was now near midnight—dark and misty; and the clouds, rolling away to the eastward from the lofty ridges of the Rocky Mountains, were gradually obscuring the dim starlight. As the lighter vapours faded from the mountains, a thick black cloud succeeded them, and settled over the loftier peaks of the chain, faintly visible through the gloom of night, whilst a mass of fleecy scud soon overspread the whole sky. A hollow moaning sound crept through the valley, and the upper branches of the cotton woods, with their withered leaves, began to rustle with the first breath of the coming storm. Huge drops of rain fell at intervals, hissing as they dropped into the blazing fires, and pattering on the skins with which the hunters hurriedly covered the exposed baggage. The mules near the camp cropped the grass with quick and greedy bites round the circuit of their pickets, as if conscious that the storm would soon prevent their feeding, and already humped their backs as the chilling rain fell upon their flanks. The prairie wolves crept closer to the camp, and in the confusion that ensued from the hurry of the trappers to cover the perishable portions of their equipment, contrived more than once to dart off with a piece of meat, when their peculiar and mournful chiding would be heard as they fought for the possession of the ravished morsel.

B

When every thing was duly protected, the men set to work to spread their beds, those who had not troubled themselves to erect a shelter getting under the lee of the piles of packs and saddles; whilst Killbuck, disdaining even such care of his carcass, threw his buffalo robe on the bare ground, declaring his intention to " take" what was coming at all hazards, and " any how."   Selecting a high spot, he drew his knife and proceeded to cut drains round it, to prevent the water running into him as he lay ; then taking a single robe he carefully spread it, placing under the end farthest from the fire a large stone brought from the creek.   Having satisfactorily adjusted this pillow, he added another robe to the one already laid, and placed over all a Navajo blanket, supposed to be impervious to rain.   Then he divested himself of his pouch and powder-horn, which, with his rifle, he placed inside his bed, and quickly covered up lest the wet should reach them. Having performed these operations to his satisfaction, he lighted his pipe by the hissing embers of the half-extinguished fire (for by this time the rain poured in torrents), and went the rounds of the picketed animals, cautioning the guard round the camp to keep their " eyes skinned, for there would be ' powder burned' before morning."   Then returning to the fire, and kicking with his mocassined foot the slumbering ashes, he squatted down before it, and thus soliloquised :—

    " Thirty year have I been knocking about these

mountains from Missoura's head as far sothe as the
starving Gila. I've trapped a ' heap,'* and many a
hundred pack of beaver I've traded in my time,
wagh! What has come of it, and whar's the dollars
as ought to be in my possibles? Whar's the ind of
this, I say? Is a man to be hunted by Injuns all
his days? Many's the time I've said I'd strike for
Taos, and trap a squaw, for this child's getting old,
and feels like wanting a woman's face about his
lodge for the balance of his days; but when it comes
to caching of the old traps, I've the smallest kind of
heart, I have. Certain, the old state comes across
my mind now and again, but who's thar to remember my old body? But them diggings gets too
over crowded now-a-days, and its hard to fetch breath
amongst them big bands of corncrackers to Missoura.
Beside, it goes against natur to leave bufler meat
and feed on hog; and them white gals are too much
like picturs, and a deal too ' fofarraw' (fanfaron).
No; darn the settlements, I say. It won't shine,
and whar's the dollars? Howsever, beaver's ' bound
to rise;' human natur can't go on selling beaver a
dollar a pound; no, no, that arn't a going to shine
much longer, I know. Them was the times when
this child first went to the mountains: six dollars
the plew—old 'un or kitten. Wagh! but its bound
to rise, I says agin; and hyar's a coon knows whar

* An Indian is always a " heap" hungry or thirsty—loves a
" heap"—is a " heap" brave—in fact, " heap" is tantamount to
very much.

to lay his hand on a dozen pack right handy, and then he'll take the Taos trail, wagh!"

Thus soliloquising, Killbuck knocked the ashes from his pipe, and placed it in the gaily ornamented case that hung round his neck, drew his knife-belt a couple of holes tighter, resumed his pouch and powder-horn, took his rifle, which he carefully covered with the folds of his Navajo blanket, and striding into the darkness, cautiously reconnoitred the vicinity of the camp. When he returned to the fire he sat himself down as before, but this time with his rifle across his lap; and at intervals his keen gray eye glanced piercingly around, particularly towards an old, weatherbeaten, and grizzled mule, who now, old stager as she was, having filled her belly, stood lazily over her picket pin, with her head bent down and her long ears flapping over her face, her limbs gathered under her, and her back arched to throw off the rain, tottering from side to side as she rested and slept.

" Yep, old gal!" cried Killbuck to the animal, at the same time picking a piece of burnt wood from the fire and throwing it at her, at which the mule gathered itself up and cocked her ears as she recognised her master's voice. " Yep, old gal! and keep your nose open; thar's brown skin about, I'm thinkin', and maybe you'll get ' roped' (lasso'd) by a Rapaho afore mornin." Again the old trapper settled himself before the fire; and soon his head began to nod, as drowsiness stole over him. Al-

ready he was in the land of dreams ; revelling
amongst bands of "fat cow," or hunting along a
stream well peopled with beaver; with no Indian
"sign" to disturb him, and the merry rendezvous
in close perspective, and his peltry selling briskly
at six dollars the plew, and galore of alcohol to
ratify the trade.   Or, perhaps, threading the back
trail of his memory, he passed rapidly through the
perilous vicissitudes of his hard, hard life—starving
one day, revelling in abundance the next; now
beset by whooping savages thirsting for his blood,
baying his enemies like the hunted deer, but with
the unflinching courage of a man; now, all care
thrown aside, secure and forgetful of the past, a
welcome guest in the hospitable trading fort; or
back, as the trail gets fainter, to his childhood's
home in the brown forests of old Kentuck, tended
and cared for—his only thought to enjoy the homminy and johnny cakes of his thrifty mother. Once
more, in warm and well remembered homespun, he
sits on the snake fence round the old clearing, and
munching his hoe-cake at set of sun, listens to the
mournful note of the whip-poor-will, or the harsh
cry of the noisy catbird, or watches the agile gam-
bols of the squirrels as they chase each other, chattering the while, from branch to branch of the lofty
tamarisks, wondering how long it will be before he
will be able to lift his father's heavy rifle, and use
it against the tempting game.   Sleep, however, sat
lightly on the eyes of the wary mountaineer, and a

snort from the old mule in an instant stretched his
every nerve. Without a movement of his body,
his keen eye fixed itself upon the mule, which now
stood with head bent round, and eyes and ears
pointed in one direction, snuffing the night air and
snorting with apparent fear. A low sound from the
wakeful hunter roused the others from their sleep;
and raising their bodies from their well-soaked beds,
a single word apprised them of their danger.

" Injuns ! "

Scarcely was the word out of Killbuck's lips,
when, above the howling of the furious wind, and
the pattering of the rain, a hundred savage yells
broke suddenly upon their ears from all directions
round the camp; a score of rifle-shots rattled from
the thicket, and a cloud of arrows whistled through
the air, whilst a crowd of Indians charged upon the
picketed animals. " Owgh, owgh—owgh—owgh—
g-h-h." " A foot, by gor ! " shouted Killbuck, " and
the old mule gone at that. On 'em, boys, for old
Kentuck ! " And he rushed towards his mule, which
jumped and snorted mad with fright, as a naked
Indian strove to fasten a lariat round her nose,
having already cut the rope which fastened her to
the picket-pin.

" Quit that, you cussed devil ! " roared the trapper, as he jumped upon the savage, and without
raising his rifle to his shoulder, made a deliberate
thrust with the muzzle at his naked breast, striking
him full, and at the same time pulling the trigger,

actually driving the Indian two paces backwards
with the shock, when he fell in a heap, and dead.
But at the same moment, an Indian, sweeping his
club round his head, brought it with fatal force down
upon Killbuck ; for a moment the hunter staggered,
threw out his arms wildly into the air, and fell
headlong to the ground.

"Owgh! owgh, owgh-h-h!" cried the Rapaho,
and, striding over the prostrate body, he seized
with his left hand the middle lock of the trapper's
long hair, and drew his knife round the head to
separate the scalp from the skull. As he bent over
to his work, the trapper named La Bonté saw his
companion's peril, rushed quick as thought at the
Indian, and buried his knife to the hilt between his
shoulders. With a gasping shudder the Rapaho
fell dead upon the prostrate body of his foe.

The attack, however, lasted but a few seconds.
The dash at the animals had been entirely successful, and, driving them before them, with loud cries,
the Indians disappeared quickly in the darkness.
Without waiting for daylight, two of the three trappers who alone were to be seen, and who had been
within the shanties at the time of attack, without a
moment's delay commenced packing two horses,
which having been fastened to the shanties had
escaped the Indians, and placing their squaws upon
them, showering curses and imprecations on their
enemies, left the camp, fearful of another onset, and
resolved to retreat and câche themselves until the

danger was over. Not so La Bonté, who, stout and
true, had done his best in the fight, and now sought
the body of his old comrade, from which, before he
could examine the wounds, he had first to remove
the corpse of the Indian he had slain. Killbuck still
breathed. He had been stunned; but, revived by
the cold rain beating upon his face, he soon opened
his eyes, and recognised his trusty friend, who,
sitting down, lifted his head into his lap, and wiped
away the blood that streamed from the wounded
scalp.

" Is the top-knot gone, boy?" asked Killbuck;
" for my head feels queersome, I tell you."

" Thar's the Injun as felt like lifting it," answered the other, kicking the dead body with his
foot.

" Wagh! boy, you've struck a coup; so scalp
the nigger right off, and then fetch me a drink."

The morning broke clear and cold. With the
exception of a light cloud which hung over Pike's
Peak, the sky was spotless; and a perfect calm had
succeeded the boisterous storm of the previous
night. The creek was swollen and turbid with the
rains; and as La Bonté proceeded a little distance
down the bank to find a passage to the water, he
suddenly stopped short, and an involuntary cry
escaped him. Within a few feet of the bank lay
the body of one of his companions, who had formed
the guard at the time of the Indians' attack. It
was lying on the face, pierced through the chest

with an arrow which was buried to the very
feathers, and the scalp torn from the bloody skull.
Beyond, but all within a hundred yards, lay the
three others, dead, and similarly mutilated. So
certain had been the aim, and so close the enemy,
that each had died without a struggle, and consequently had been unable to alarm the camp. La
Bonté, with a glance at the bank, saw at once that
the wily Indians had crept along the creek, the
noise of the storm facilitating their approach undiscovered, and crawling up the bank, had watched
their opportunity to shoot simultaneously the four
hunters on guard.

Returning to Killbuck, he apprised him of the
melancholy fate of their companions, and held a
council of war as to their proceedings. The old
hunter's mind was soon made up. " First," said
he, " I get back my old mule ; she's carried me and
my traps these twelve years, and I aint a goin' to
lose her yet. Second, I feel like taking hair, and
some Rapahos has to ' go under ' for this night's
work. Third, We have got to câche the beaver.
Fourth, We take the Injun trail, wherever it
leads."

No more daring mountaineer than La Bonté
ever trapped a beaver, and no counsel could have
more exactly tallied with his own inclination than
the law laid down by old Killbuck.

" Agreed," was his answer, and forthwith he set
about forming a câche. In this instance they had

not sufficient time to construct a regular one, so
they contented themselves with securing their packs
of beaver in buffalo robes, and tying them in the
forks of several cotton-woods, under which the camp
had been made. This done, they lit a fire, and
cooked some buffalo meat; and, whilst smoking a
pipe, carefully cleaned their rifles, and filled their
horns and pouches with good store of ammunition.

A prominent feature in the character of the hunters of the far west is their quick determination and
resolve in cases of extreme difficulty and peril, and
their fixedness of purpose, when any plan of opera--
tions has been laid requiring bold and instant action
in carrying out. It is here that they so infinitely
surpass the savage Indian, in bringing to a successful issue their numerous hostile expeditions against
the natural foe of the white man in the wild and
barbarous regions of the west. Ready to resolve
as they are prompt to execute, and combining far
greater dash and daring with equal subtlety and
caution, they possess great advantage over the vacil-
lating Indian, whose superstitious mind in a great
degree paralyses the physical energy of his active
body; and who, by waiting for propitious signs and
seasons before he undertakes an enterprise, often
loses the opportunity by which his white and more
civilised enemy knows so well how to profit.

Killbuck and La Bonté were no exceptions to this
characteristic rule; and before the sun was a hand's-
breadth above the eastern horizon, the two hunters

were running on the trail of the victorious Indians. Striking from the creek where the night attack was made, they crossed to another known as Kioway, running parallel to Bijou, a few hours' journey westward, and likewise heading in the " divide." Following this to its forks, they struck into the upland prairies lying at the foot of the mountains; and crossing to the numerous water-courses which feed the creek called " Vermillion" or " Cherry," they pursued the trail over the mountain-spurs until it reached a fork of the Boiling Spring. Here the war-party had halted and held a consultation, for from this point the trail turned at a tangent to the westward, and entered the rugged gorges of the mountains. It was now evident to the two trappers that their destination was the Bayou Salade,—a mountain valley which is a favourite resort of the buffalo in the winter season, and which, and for this reason, is often frequented by the Yuta Indians as their wintering ground. That the Rapahos were on a war expedition against the Yutas, there was little doubt; and Killbuck, who knew every inch of the ground, saw at once, by the direction the trail had taken, that they were making for the Bayou in order to surprise their enemies, and, therefore, were not following the usual Indian trail up the canon of the Boiling Spring River. Having made up his mind to this, he at once struck across the broken ground lying at the foot of the mountains, steering a course a little to the eastward of north, or almost in the

direction whence he had come : and then, pointing
westward, about noon he crossed a mountain chain,
and descending into a ravine through which a little
rivulet tumbled over its rocky bed, he at once proved
the correctness of his judgment by striking the
Indian trail, now quite fresh, as it wound through the
canon along the bank of the stream. The route he
had followed, impracticable to pack-animals, had
saved at least half-a-day's journey, and brought
them within a short distance of the object of their
pursuit; for, at the head of the gorge, a lofty bluff
presenting itself, the hunters ascended to the summit, and, looking down, descried at their very feet
the Indian camp, with their own stolen cavallada
feeding quietly round.

" Wagh!" exclaimed both the hunters in a
breath. "And thar's the old ga'l at that," chuckled
Killbuck, as he recognised his old grizzled mule
making good play at the rich buffalo grass with
which these mountain valleys abound.

" If we don't make ' a raise' afore long, I wouldn't
say so. Thar plans is plain to this child as beaver
sign. They're after Yuta hair, as certain as this
gun has got hind-sights; but they ar'nt agoin' to
pack them animals after 'em, and have crawled like
' rattlers' along this bottom to câche 'em till they
come back from the Bayou,—and maybe they'll
leave half a dozen ' soldiers'* with 'em."

---

* The young untried warriors of the Indians are thus called.

How right the wily trapper was in his conjectures will be shortly proved. Meanwhile, with his companion, he descended the bluff, and pushing his way into a thicket of dwarf pine and cedar, sat down on a log, and drew from an end of the blanket, strapped on his shoulder, a portion of a buffalo's liver, which they both discussed, *raw*, with infinite relish; eating in lieu of bread (an unknown luxury in these parts) sundry strips of dried fat. To have kindled a fire would have been dangerous, since it was not impossible that some of the Indians might leave their camp to hunt, when the smoke would at once have betrayed the presence of enemies. A light was struck, however for their pipes, and after enjoying this true consolation for some time, they laid a blanket on the ground, and, side by side, soon fell asleep.

If Killbuck had been a prophet, or the most prescient of "medicine men," he could not have more exactly predicted the movements in the Indian camp. About three hours before "sun-down," he rose and shook himself, which movement was sufficient to awaken his companion. Telling La Bonté to lie down again and rest, he gave him to understand that he was about to reconnoitre the enemy's camp; and after carefully examining his rifle, and drawing his knife-belt a hole or two tighter, he proceeded on his dangerous errand. Ascending the same bluff whence he had first discovered the Indian camp, he glanced rapidly around, and made himself master of

the features of the ground—choosing a ravine by
which he might approach the camp more closely,
and without danger of being discovered. This was
soon effected; and in half an hour the trapper was
lying on his belly on the summit of a pine-covered
bluff, which overlooked the Indians within easy rifle-
shot, and so perfectly concealed by the low spreading branches of the cedar and arbor-vitæ, that not
a particle of his person could be detected; unless,
indeed, his sharp twinkling gray eye contrasted too
strongly with the green boughs that covered the
rest of his face. Moreover, there was no danger of
their hitting upon his trail, for he had been careful
to pick his steps on the rock-covered ground, so
that not a track of his moccasin was visible. Here
he lay, still as a carcagien in wait for a deer, only
now and then shaking the boughs as his body qui-
vered with a suppressed chuckle, when any movement in the Indian camp caused him to laugh in-
wardly at his (if they had known it) unwelcome
propinquity. He was not a little surprised, however,
to discover that the party was much smaller than
he had imagined, counting only forty warriors; and
this assured him that the band had divided, one
half taking the Yuta trail by the Boiling Spring, the
other (the one before him) taking a longer circuit
in order to reach the Bayou, and make the attack
on the Yutas in a different direction.

At this moment the Indians were in delibera-
tion. Seated in a large circle round a very small

fire,* the smoke from which ascended in a thin
straight column, they each in turn puffed a huge cloud
of smoke from three or four long cherry-stemmed
pipes, which went the round of the party; each
warrior touching the ground with the heel of the
pipe-bowl, and turning the stem upwards and away
from him as "medicine" to the Great Spirit, before
he himself inhaled the fragrant kinnik-kinnik. The
council, however, was not general, for only fifteen
of the older warriors took part in it, the others sitting outside and at some little distance from the
circle. Behind each were his arms—bow and quiver,
and shield hanging from a spear stuck in the ground,
and a few guns in ornamented covers of buckskin
were added to some of the equipments.

Near the fire, and in the centre of the inner circle,
a spear was fixed upright in the ground, and on this
dangled the four scalps of the trappers killed the
preceding night; and underneath them, affixed to
the same spear, was the mystic "medicine bag," by
which Killbuck knew that the band before him was
under the command of the chief of the tribe.

Towards the grim trophies on the spear, the warriors, who in turn addressed the council, frequently
pointed—more than one, as he did so, making the

---

* There is a great difference between an Indian's fire and
a white's. The former places the ends of logs to burn gradually; the latter, the centre, besides making such a bonfire that
the Indians truly say, "The white makes a fire so hot that he
cannot approach to warm himself by it."

gyratory motion of the right hand and arm, which
the Indians use in describing that they have gained
an advantage by skill or cunning. Then pointing westward, the speaker would thrust out his
arm, extending his fingers at the same time, and
closing and reopening them repeatedly, meaning,
that although four scalps already ornamented the
"medicine" pole, they were as nothing compared
to the numerous trophies they would bring from the
Salt Valley, where they expected to find their here-
ditary enemies the Yutas. "That now was not the
time to count their coups," (for at this moment one
of the warriors rose from his seat, and, swelling
with pride, advanced towards the spear, pointing to
one of the scalps, and then striking his open hand
on his naked breast, jumped into the air, as if about
to go through the ceremony). "That before many
suns all their spears together would not hold the
scalps they had taken, and that they would return
to their village and spend a moon relating their
achievements, and counting coups."

All this Killbuck learned : thanks to his knowledge of the language of signs—a master of which,
if even he have no ears or tongue, never fails to
understand, and be understood by, any of the hundred tribes whose languages are perfectly distinct
and different. He learned, moreover, that at sundown the greater part of the band would resume
the trail, in order to reach the Bayou by the ear-
liest dawn ; and also, that no more than four or five

of the younger warriors would remain with the captured animals. Still the hunter remained in his position until the sun had disappeared behind the ridge; when, taking up their arms, and throwing their buffalo robes on their shoulders, the war party of Rapahos, one behind the other, with noiseless step, and silent as the dumb, moved away from the camp. When the last dusky form had disappeared behind a point of rocks which shut in the northern end of the little valley or ravine, Killbuck withdrew his head from its screen, crawled backwards on his stomach from the edge of the bluff, and, rising from the ground, shook and stretched himself; then gave one cautious look around, and immediately proceeded to rejoin his companion.

"*Lave* (get up), boy," said Killbuck, as soon as he reached him. "Hyar's grainin' to do afore long—and sun's about down, I'm thinking."

"Ready, old hos," answered La Bonté, giving himself a shake. "What's the sign like, and how many's the lodge?"

"Fresh, and five, boy. How do you feel?"

"*Half froze for hair.* Wagh!"

"We'll have moon to-night, and as soon as *she* gets up, we'll make 'em ' come.' "

Killbuck then described to his companion what he had seen, and detailed his plan. This was simply to wait until the moon afforded sufficient light, then to approach the Indian camp and charge into it, " lift" as much " hair" as they could, recover their ani-

C

mals, and start at once to the Bayou and join the
friendly Yutas, warning them of the coming danger.
The risk of falling in with either of the Rapaho
bands was hardly considered; to avoid this, they
trusted to their own foresight, and the legs of their
mules, should they encounter them

Between sundown and the rising of the moon,
they had leisure to eat their supper, which, as before, consisted of raw buffalo-liver; after discussing
which, Killbuck pronounced himself " a ' heap' better," and ready for " huggin."

In the short interval of almost perfect darkness
which preceded the moonlight, and taking advantage of one of the frequent squalls of wind which
howl down the narrow gorges of the mountains;
these two determined men, with footsteps noiseless
as the panther's, crawled to the edge of the little
plateau of some hundred yards' square, where the
five Indians in charge of the animals were seated
round the fire, perfectly unconscious of the vicinity
of danger.   Several clumps of cedar bushes dotted
the small prairie, and amongst these the well-hobbled
mules and horses were feeding.   These animals,
accustomed to the presence of whites, would not
notice the two hunters as they crept from clump to
clump nearer to the fire, and also served, even if
the Indians should be on the watch, to conceal their
movements from them.

This the two men at once perceived; but old Killbuck knew that if he passed within sight or smell

of his mule, he would be received with a hinny of
recognition, which would at once alarm the enemy.
He therefore first ascertained where his own animal
was feeding, which luckily was at the farther side
of the prairie, and would not interfere with his proceedings.

Threading their way amongst the feeding mules,
they approached a clump of bushes about forty
yards from the spot where the unconscious savages
were seated smoking round the fire; and here they
awaited, scarcely drawing breath the while, the
moment when the moon rose above the mountain
into the clear cold sky, and gave them light sufficient to make sure their work of bloody retribution.
Not a pulsation in the hearts of these stern determined men beat higher than its wont; not the tre-
mour of a nerve disturbed their frame.   They stood
with lips compressed and rifles ready, their pistols
loosened in their belts, their scalp-knives handy to
their gripe.   The lurid glow of the coming moon
already shot into the sky above the ridge, which
stood out in bold relief against the light; and the
luminary herself just peered over the mountain,
illuminating its pine-clad summit, and throwing her
beams on an opposite peak, when Killbuck touched
his companion's arm, and whispered, " Wait for the
full light, boy."

At this moment, however, unseen by the trapper,
the old grizzled mule had gradually approached, as
she fed along the plateau; and, when within a few

paces of their retreat, a gleam of moonshine revealed
to the animal the erect forms of the two whites.
Suddenly she stood still and pricked her ears, and
stretching out her neck and nose, snuffed the air.
Well she knew her old master.

Killbuck, with eyes fixed upon the Indians, was
on the point of giving the signal of attack to his
comrade, when the shrill hinny of his mule rever-
berated through the gorge. The Indians jumped
to their feet and seized their arms, when Killbuck,
with a loud shout of " At 'em boy ; give the niggurs
h—!" rushed from his concealment, and with La
Bonté by his side, yelling a fierce war-whoop,
sprung upon the startled savages.

Panic-struck with the suddenness of the attack,
the Indians scarcely knew where to run, and for a
moment stood huddled together like sheep. Down
dropped Killbuck on his knee, and stretching out
his wiping-stick, planted it on the ground at the
extreme length of his arm. As methodically and
as coolly as if about to aim at a deer, he raised his
rifle to this rest and pulled the trigger. At the
report an Indian fell forward on his face, at the
same moment that La Bonté, with equal certainty
of aim and like effect, discharged his own rifle.

The three surviving Indians, seeing that their
assailants were but two, and knowing that their
guns were empty, came on with loud yells. With
the left hand grasping a bunch of arrows, and holding the bow already bent and arrow fixed, they

steadily advanced, bending low to the ground to get their objects between them and the light, and thus render their aim more certain. The trappers, however, did not care to wait for them. Drawing their pistols, they charged at once; and although the bows twanged, and the three arrows struck their mark, on they rushed, discharging their pistols at close quarters. La Bonté threw his empty one at the head of an Indian who was pulling his second arrow to its head at a yard's distance, drew his knife at the same moment, and made at him.

But the Indian broke and ran, followed by his surviving companion; and as soon as Killbuck could ram home another ball, he sent a shot flying after them as they scrambled up the mountain side, leaving in their fright and hurry their bows and shields on the ground.

The fight was over, and the two trappers confronted each other:—" We've given 'em h—!" laughed Killbuck.

" *Well*, we have," answered the other, pulling an arrow out of his arm.—" Wagh!"

" We'll lift the hair, any how," continued the first, " afore the scalp's cold."

Taking his whetstone from the little sheath on his knife-belt, the trapper proceeded to " edge " his knife, and then stepping to the first prostrate body, he turned it over to examine if any symptom of vitality remained. " Thrown cold!" he exclaimed, as he dropped the lifeless arm he had lifted.

" I sighted him about the long ribs, but the light
was bad, and I couldn't get a ' bead' ' off hand '
any how."

Seizing with his left hand the long and braided
lock on the centre of the Indian's head, he passed
the point edge of his keen butcher-knife round the
parting, turning it at the same time under the skin
to separate the scalp from the skull ; then, with a
quick and sudden jerk of his hand, he removed it
entirely from the head, and giving the reeking
trophy a wring upon the grass to free it from the
blood, he coolly hitched it under his belt, and proceeded to the next ; but seeing La Bonté operating
upon this, he sought the third, who lay some little
distance from the others.   This one was still alive,
a pistol-ball having passed through his body, without touching a vital spot.

" Gut-shot is this niggur," exclaimed the trapper ; " them pistols never throws 'em in their
tracks ;" and thrusting his knife, for mercy's
sake, into the bosom of the Indian, he likewise
tore the scalp-lock from his head, and placed it
with the other.

La Bonté had received two trivial wounds, and
Killbuck till now had been walking about with an
arrow sticking through the fleshy part of his thigh,
the point being perceptible near the surface of the
other side.   To free his leg from the painful encum-
brance, he thrust the weapon completely through,
and then, cutting off the arrow-head below the

barb, he drew it out, the blood flowing freely from the wound. A tourniquet of buckskin soon stopped this, and, heedless of the pain, the hardy mountaineer sought for his old mule, and quickly brought it to the fire (which La Bonté had rekindled), lavishing many a caress, and most comical terms of endearment, upon the faithful companion of his wanderings. They found all the animals safe and well; and after eating heartily of some venison which the Indians had been cooking at the moment of the attack, made instant preparations to quit the scene of their exploit, not wishing to trust to the chance of the Rapahos being too frightened to again molest them.

Having no saddles, they secured buffalo robes on the backs of two mules—Killbuck, of course, riding his own—and lost no time in proceeding on their way. They followed the course of the Indians up the stream, and found that it kept the cañons and gorges of the mountains, where the road was better; but it was with no little difficulty that they made their way, the ground being much broken, and covered with rocks. Killbuck's wound became very painful, and his leg stiffened and swelled distressingly, but he still pushed on all night, and, at daybreak, recognising their position, he left the Indian trail, and followed a little creek which rose in a mountain chain of moderate elevation, and above which, and to the south, Pike's Peak towered high into the clouds. With great difficulty they crossed this ridge, and ascending and descending several smaller ones, which gradually smoothed away as they met the valley, about three hours after sunrise they found themselves in the south-east corner of the Bayou Salade.

The Bayou Salade, or Salt Valley, is the most southern of three very extensive valleys, forming a series of table-lands in the very centre of the main chain of the Rocky Mountains, known to the trappers by the name of the " Parks." The numerous streams by which they are watered abound in the valuable fur-bearing beaver, whilst every species of game common to the west is found here in great abundance. The Bayou Salade especially, owing to the salitrose nature of the soil and springs, is the favourite resort of all the larger animals common to the mountains; and, in the sheltered prairies of the Bayou, the buffalo, forsaking the barren and inclement regions of the exposed plains, frequent these upland valleys, in the winter months; and feeding upon the rich and nutritious buffalo grass which, on the bare prairies, at that season, is either dry and rotten, or entirely exhausted, not only sustain life, but retain a great portion of the " condition " that the abundant fall and summer pasture of the lowlands has laid upon their bones. Therefore is this valley sought by the Indians as a wintering ground. Its occupancy has been disputed by most of the mountain tribes, and long and bloody wars have been waged to make good the claims set

forth by Yuta, Rapaho, Sioux, and Shians. However, to the first of these it may be said now to
belong, since their " big village" has wintered
there for many successive years ; whilst the Rapahos seldom visit it unless on war expeditions against
the Yutas.

Judging, from the direction the Rapahos were
taking, that the friendly tribe of Yutas were there
already, the trappers had resolved to join them as
soon as possible ; and therefore, without resting,
pushed on through the uplands, and, towards the
middle of the day, had the satisfaction of descrying
the conical lodges of the village, situated on a large
level plateau, through which ran a mountain stream.
A numerous band of mules and horses were scattered over the pasture, and round them several
mounted Indians kept guard.   As the trappers
descended the bluffs into the plain, some straggling
Indians caught sight of them ; and instantly one of
them, lassoing a horse from the herd, mounted it,
barebacked, and flew like wind to the village to
spread the news.   Soon the lodges disgorged their
inmates ; first the women and children rushed to
the side of the strangers' approach ; then the
younger Indians, unable to restrain their curiosity, mounted their horses, and galloped forth to
meet them.   The old chiefs, enveloped in buffalo
robes (softly and delicately dressed as the Yutas
alone know how), and with tomahawk held in one
hand and resting in the hollow of the other arm,

sallied last of all from their lodges, and, squatting in a row on a sunny bank outside the village, awaited, with dignified composure, the arrival of the whites. Killbuck was well known to most of them, having trapped in their country and traded with them years before at Roubideau's fort at the head waters of the Rio Grande. After shaking hands with all who presented themselves, he at once gave them to understand that their enemies, the Rapahos, were at hand, with a hundred warriors at least, elated by the coup they had just struck against the whites, bringing, moreover, four white scalps to incite them to brave deeds.

At this news the whole village was speedily in commotion: the war-shout was taken up from lodge to lodge; the squaws began to lament and tear their hair; the warriors to paint and arm themselves. The elder chiefs immediately met in council, and, over the medicine-pipe, debated as to the best course to pursue,—whether to wait the attack, or sally out and meet the enemy. In the mean time, the braves were collected together by the chiefs of their respective bands, and scouts, mounted on the fastest horses, despatched in every direction to procure intelligence of the enemy.

The two whites, after watering their mules and picketing them in some good grass near the village, drew near the council fire, without, however, joining in the " talk," until they were invited to take their seats by the eldest chief. Then Killbuck was

called upon to give his opinion as to the direction
in which he judged the Rapahos to be approaching,
which he delivered in their own language, with which
he was well acquainted. In a short time the council
broke up, and, without noise or confusion, a band of
one hundred chosen warriors left the village, immediately after one of the scouts had galloped in and
communicated some intelligence to the chiefs. Killbuck and La Bonté volunteered to accompany the
war-party, weak and exhausted as they were; but
this was negatived by the chiefs, who left their white
brothers to the care of the women, who tended their
wounds, now stiff and painful : and spreading their
buffalo robes in a warm and roomy lodge, left them
to the repose they so much needed.

CHAPTER II.

THE next morning, Killbuck's leg was greatly in-
flamed, and he was unable to leave the lodge; but
he made his companion bring the old mule to the
door, that he might give her a couple of ears of
Indian corn, the last remains of the slender store
brought by the Indians from the Navajo country.
The day passed, and sundown brought no tidings of
the war-party. This caused no little wailing on the
part of the squaws, but was interpreted by the
whites as a favourable augury. A little after sunrise, on the second morning, the long line of the
returning warriors was discerned winding over the
prairie, and a scout having galloped in to bring the
news of a great victory, the whole village was soon
in a ferment of paint and drumming. A short distance from the lodges, the warriors halted to await
the approach of the people. Old men, children, and
squaws sitting astride their horses, sallied out to escort the victorious party in triumph to the village.
With loud shouts and songs, and drums beating the
monotonous Indian time, they advanced and encircled
the returning braves, one of whom, his face covered
with black paint, carried a pole on which dangled

thirteen scalps, the trophies of the expedition.   As
he lifted these on high, they were saluted with deafening whoops and cries of exultation and savage joy.
In this manner they entered the village, almost
before the friends of those fallen in the fight had
ascertained their losses. Then the shouts of delight
were converted into yells of grief; the mothers and
wives of those braves who had been killed (and seven
had " gone under") presently returned with their
faces, necks, and hands blackened, and danced and
howled round the scalp-pole, which had been deposited in the centre of the village, in front of the
lodge of the great chief.

Killbuck now learned that a scout having brought
intelligence that the two bands of Rapahos were
hastening to form a junction, as soon as they learned
that their approach was discovered, the Yutas had
successfully prevented it; and attacking one party,
had entirely defeated it, killing thirteen of the
Rapaho braves. The other party had fled on seeing
the issue of the fight, and a few of the Yuta warriors
were now pursuing them.

To celebrate so signal a victory, great preparations sounded their notes through the village. Paints,
—vermilion and ochres—red and yellow,—were in
great request; whilst the scrapings of charred wood,
mixed with gunpowder, were used as substitute for
black, the medicine colour.

The lodges of the village, numbering some two

hundred or more, were erected in parallel lines, and
covered a large space of the level prairie in shape
of a parallelogram. In the centre, however, the
space which half a dozen lodges in length would
have taken up was left unoccupied, save by one large
one, of red-painted buffalo skins, tatooed with the
mystic totems of the "medicine" peculiar to the
nation. In front of this stood the grim scalp-pole,
like a decayed tree trunk, its bloody fruit tossing in
the wind; and on another pole, at a few feet distance,
was hung the " bag" with its mysterious contents.
Before each lodge a tripod of spears supported the
arms and shields of the Yuta chivalry, and on many
of them, smoke-dried scalps rattled in the wind,
former trophies of the dusky knights who were
arming themselves within. Heraldic devices were not
wanting,—not, however, graved upon the shield, but
hanging from the spear-head, the actual " totem"
of the warrior it distinguished. The rattlesnake, the
otter, the carcagien, the mountain badger, the war-
eagle, the kon-qua-kish, the porcupine, the fox, &c.,
dangled their well-stuffed skins, displaying the guar-
dian " medicine" of the warriors they pertained to,
and representing the mental and corporeal qualities
which were supposed to characterise the braves to
whom they belonged.

From the centre lodge, two or three " medicine
men," fantastically attired in the skins of wolves and
bears, and bearing long peeled wands of cherry in

their hands, occasionally emerged to tend a very
small fire which they had kindled in the centre of
the open space; and, when a thin column of smoke
arose, one of them planted the scalp-pole obliquely
across the fire. Squaws in robes of white dressed
buckskin, garnished with beads and porcupines'
quills, and their faces painted bright red and black,
then appeared. These ranged themselves round
the outside of the square, the boys and children of
all ages, mounted on bare-backed horses, galloping
round and round, and screaming with eagerness,
excitement, and curiosity.

Presently the braves and warriors made their
appearance, and squatted round the fire in two
circles, those who had been engaged on the expedition being in the first or smaller one. One medicine
man sat under the scalp-pole, having a drum between
his knees, which he tapped at intervals with his
hand, eliciting from the instrument a hollow monotonous sound. A bevy of women, shoulder to shoulder, then advanced from the four sides of the square,
and some, shaking a rattle-drum in time with their
steps, commenced a jumping jerking dance, now lifting one foot from the ground, and now rising with
both, accompanying the dance with a chant, which
swelled from a low whisper to the utmost extent
of their voices—now dying away, and again burst-
ing into vociferous measure. Thus they advanced
to the centre and retreated to their former positions;
when six squaws, with their faces painted a dead

black, made their appearance from the crowd, chant-
ing, in soft and sweet measure, a lament for the
braves the nation had lost in the late battle : but
soon as they drew near the scalp-pole, their melancholy note changed to the music (to them) of grati-
fied revenge.   In a succession of jumps, raising the
feet alternately but a little distance from the ground,
they made their way, through an interval left in the
circle of warriors, to the grim pole, and encircling
it, danced in perfect silence round it for a few
moments.   Then they burst forth with an extem-
pore song, laudatory of the achievements of their
victorious braves.   They addressed the scalps as
" sisters" (to be called a squaw is the greatest insult
that can be offered to an Indian), and, spitting at
them, upbraided them with their rashness in leaving
their lodges to seek for Yuta husbands ; " that the
Yuta warriors and young men despised them, and
chastised them for their forwardness and pre-
sumption, bringing back their scalps to their own
women."

After sufficiently proving that they had any thing
but lost the use of their tongues, but possessed, on
the contrary, as fair a length of that formidable
weapon as any of their sex, they withdrew, and left
the field in undisputed possession of the men : who,
accompanied by tap of drum, and by the noise of
many rattles, broke out into a war-song, in which
their own valour was by no means hidden in a
bushel, or modestly refused the light of day.   After

this came the more interesting ceremony of a warrior " counting his coups."

A young brave, with his face painted black, mounted on a white horse mysteriously marked with red clay, and naked to the breech-clout, holding in his hand a long taper lance, rode into the circle, and paced slowly round it; then, flourishing his spear on high, he darted to the scalp-pole, round which the warriors were now seated in a semicircle; and in a loud voice, and with furious gesticulations, related his exploits, the drums tapping at the conclusion of each. On his spear hung seven scalps, and holding it vertically above his head, and commencing with the top one, he told the feats in which he had raised the trophy hair. When he had run through these, the drums tapped loudly, and several of the old chiefs shook their rattles, in corroboration of the truth of his achievements. The brave, swelling with pride, then pointed to the fresh and bloody scalps hanging on the pole. Two of these had been torn from the heads of Rapahos struck by his own hand, and this feat, *the* exploit of the day, had entitled him to the honour of counting his coups. Then, sticking his spear into the ground by the side of the pole, he struck his hand twice on his brawny and naked chest, turned short round, and, swift as the antelope, galloped into the plain : as if overcome by the shock his modesty had received in being obliged to recount his own high-sounding deeds.

" Wagh!" exclaimed old Killbuck, as he left the

D

circle, pointing his pipe-stem towards the fast-
fading figure of the brave, " that Injun's heart's
about as big as ever it will be, I'm thinking."

With the Yutas, Killbuck and La Bonté remained
during the winter; and when the spring sun had
opened the ice-bound creeks, and melted the snow
on the mountains, and its genial warmth had
expanded the earth and permitted the roots of the
grass to " live" once more, and throw out green and
tender shoots, the two trappers bade adieu to the
hospitable Indians, who broke up their village in
order to start for the valleys of the Del Norte. As
they followed the trail from the bayou, at sundown,
just as they thought of camping, they observed
ahead of them a solitary horseman riding along,
followed by three mules. His hunting-frock of
fringed buckskin, and the rifle resting across the
horn of his saddle, at once proclaimed him white;
but as he saw the mountaineers winding through
the cañon, driving before them half a dozen horses,
he judged they might possibly be Indians and enemies, the more so as their dress was not the usual
costume of the whites. The trappers, therefore, saw
the stranger raise the rifle in the hollow of his arm,
and, gathering up his horse, ride steadily to meet
them, as soon as he observed they were but two;
two to one in mountain calculation being scarcely
considered odds, if red skin to white.

However, on nearing them, the stranger discovered his mistake; and, throwing his rifle across

the saddle once more, reined in his horse and waited their approach ; for the spot where he then
stood presented an excellent camping-ground, with
abundance of dry wood and convenient water.

" Where from, stranger ?"

" The divide, and to the bayou for meat ; and
you are from there, I see. Any buffalo come in
yet ?"

" Heap, and seal-fat at that. What's the sign
out on the plains ? "

" War-party of Rapahos passed Squirrel at sundown yesterday, and nearly raised my animals.
Sign, too, of more on left fork of Boiling Spring.
No buffalo between this and Bijou. Do you feel
like camping ? "

" *Well*, we do. But whar's your companyeros ?"

" I'm alone."

" Alone ! Wagh ! how do you get your animals
along ? "

" I go ahead, and they follow the horse."

" Well, that beats all ! That's a smart-looking
hos now ; and runs some, I'm thinking."

" Well, it does."

" Whar's them mules from ? They look like
Californy."

" Mexican country—away down south."

" H—! Whar's yourself from ? "

" There away, too."

" What's beaver worth in Taos ? "

" Dollar."

" In Saint Louiy ? "

" Same."

" H—! Any call for buckskin ? "

" A heap! The soldiers in Santa Fé are half froze for leather ; and moccasins fetch two dollars, easy."

" Wagh! How's trade on Arkansa, and what's doin to the Fort ? "

" Shians at Big Timber, and Bent's people trading smart. On North Fork, Jim Waters got a hundred pack right off, and Sioux making more."

" Whar's Bill Williams ? "

" Gone under, they say : the Diggers took his hair."

" How's powder goin ? "

" Two dollars a pint."

" Bacca ? "

" A plew a plug."

" Got any about you ? "

" Have *so*."

" Give us a chaw ; and now let's camp."

Whilst unpacking their own animals, the two trappers could not refrain from glancing, every now and then, with no little astonishment, at the solitary stranger they had so unexpectedly encountered. If truth be told, his appearance not a little perplexed them. His hunting-frock of buckskin, shining with grease, and fringed pantaloons, over which the well-greased butcher-knife had evidently been often wiped after cutting his food, or butcher-

ing the carcass of deer and buffalo, were of genuine
mountain make. His face, clean shaved, exhibited
in its well-tanned and weather-beaten complexion,
the effects of such natural cosmetics as sun and
wind; and under the mountain hat of felt which
covered his head, long uncut hair hung in Indian
fashion on his shoulders. All this would have
passed muster, had it not been for the most extraordinary equipment of a double-barrelled rifle;
which, when it had attracted the eyes of the mountaineers, elicited no little astonishment, not to say
derision. But, perhaps, nothing excited their ad-
miration so much as the perfect docility of the
stranger's animals; which, almost like dogs, obeyed
his voice and call; and albeit that one, in a small
sharp head and pointed ears, expanded nostrils,
and eye twinkling and malicious, exhibited the per-
sonification of a "lurking devil," yet they could
not but admire the perfect ease with which even
this one, in common with the rest, permitted herself
to be handled.

Dismounting, and unhitching from the horn of
his saddle the coil of skin rope, one end of which
was secured round the neck of the horse, he proceeded to unsaddle; and whilst so engaged, the
three mules, two of which were packed, one with
the unbutchered carcass of a deer, the other with a
pack of skins, &c., followed leisurely into the space
chosen for the camp, and, cropping the grass at

their ease, waited until a whistle called them to be unpacked.

The horse was a strong square-built bay; and, although the severities of a prolonged winter, with scanty pasture and long and trying travel, had robbed his bones of fat and flesh, tucked up his flank, and "ewed" his neck; still his clean and well-set legs, oblique shoulder, and withers fine as a deer's, in spite of his gaunt half-starved appearance, bore ample testimony as to what he *had* been; while his clear cheerful eye, and the hearty appetite with which he fell to work on the coarse grass of the bottom, proved that he had something in him still, and was game as ever. His tail, gnawed by the mules in days of strait, attracted the observant mountaineers.

" Hard doins when it come to that," remarked La Bonté.

Between the horse and two of the mules a mutual and great affection appeared to subsist, which was no more than natural, when their master observed to his companions that they had travelled together upwards of two thousand miles.

One of these mules was a short, thick-set, stumpy animal, with an enormous head surmounted by proportionable ears, and a pair of unusually large eyes, beaming the most perfect good temper and docility (most uncommon qualities in a mule.) Her neck was thick, and rendered more so in appearance by

reason of her mane not being roached, (or, in English, hogged), which privilege she alone enjoyed of
the trio ; and her short, strong legs, ending in small,
round, cat-like hoofs, were feathered with a profu-
sion of dark brown hair.

As she stood stock-still, whilst the stranger removed the awkwardly packed deer from her back,
she flapped her huge ears backward and forward,
occasionally turning her head, and laying her cold
nose against her master's cheek. When the pack
was removed, he advanced to her head, and resting
it on his shoulder, rubbed her broad and grizzled
cheeks with both his hands for several minutes, the
old mule laying her ears, like a rabbit, back upon
her neck, and with half-closed eyes enjoyed mightily the manipulation. Then, giving her a smack
upon the haunch, and a " hep-a " well known to the
mule kind, the old favourite threw up her heels and
cantered off to the horse, who was busily cropping
the buffalo grass on the bluff above the stream.

Great was the contrast between the one just described and the next which came up to be divested
of her pack. She, a tall beautifully shaped Mexican mule, of a light mouse colour, with a head like
a deer's, and long springy legs, trotted up obedient
to the call, but with ears bent back and curled up
nose, and tail compressed between her legs. As
her pack was being removed, she groaned and
whined like a dog, as a thong or loosened strap
touched her ticklish body, lifting her hind-quarters

in a succession of jumps or preparatory kicks, and looking wicked as a panther. When nothing but the fore pack-saddle remained, she had worked herself into the last stage; and as the stranger cast loose the girth of buffalo hide, and was about to lift the saddle and draw the crupper from the tail, she drew her hind legs under her, more tightly compressed her tail, and almost shrieked with rage.

"Stand clear," he roared (knowing what was coming), and raised the saddle, when out went her hind legs, up went the pack into the air, and, with it dangling at her heels, away she tore, kicking the offending saddle as she ran. Her master, however, took this as matter of course, followed her and brought back the saddle, which he piled on the others to windward of the fire one of the trappers was kindling. Fire-making is a simple process with the mountaineers. Their bullet-pouches always contain a flint and steel, and sundry pieces of "punk"* or tinder; and pulling a handful of dry grass, which they screw into a nest, they place the lighted punk in this, and, closing the grass over it, wave it in the air, when it soon ignites, and readily kindles the dry sticks forming the foundation of the fire.

The tit-bits of the deer the stranger had brought in were soon roasting over the fire; whilst, as soon as the burning logs had deposited a sufficiency of ashes, a hole was raked in them, and the head of

---

* A pithy substance found in dead pine-trees.

the deer, skin, hair, and all, placed in this primitive oven, and carefully covered with the hot ashes.

A " heap " of " fat meat " in perspective, our mountaineers enjoyed their ante-prandial pipes, recounting the news of the respective regions whence they came ; and so well did they like each other's company, so sweet was the " honey-dew " tobacco of which the strange hunter had good store, so plentiful the game about the creek, and so abundant the pasture for their winter-starved animals, that before the carcass of the " two-year " buck had been more than four-fifths consumed ; and, although rib after rib had been picked and chucked over their shoulders to the wolves, and one fore leg and *the* " bit " of all, the head, were still cooked before them,—the three had come to the resolution to join company, and hunt in their present locality for a few days at least—the owner of the " two-shoot " gun volunteering to fill their horns with powder, and find tobacco for their pipes.

Here, on plenty of meat, of venison, bear, and antelope, they merrily luxuriated ; returning after their daily hunts to the brightly burning camp-fire, where one always remained to guard the animals, and unloading their packs of meat, (all choicest portions), ate late into the night, and, smoking, wiled away the time in narrating scenes in their hard-spent lives, and fighting their battles o'er again.

The younger of the trappers, he who has figured under the name of La Bonté, had excited, by scraps

and patches from his history, no little curiosity in
the stranger's mind to learn the ups and downs of
his career; and one night, when they assembled
earlier than usual at the fire, he prevailed upon the
modest trapper to "unpack" some passages in his
wild adventurous life.

"Maybe," commenced the mountaineer, "you
both remember when old Ashley went out with the
biggest kind of band to trap the Columbia, and
head-waters of Missoura and Yellow Stone. Well,
that was the time this niggur first felt like taking
to the mountains."

This brings us back to the year of our Lord
1825; and perhaps it will be as well, in order to
render La Bonté's mountain language intelligible,
to translate it at once into tolerable English, and
to tell in the third person, but from his own lips,
the scrapes which befell him in a sojourn of more
than twenty years in the Far West, and the causes
that impelled him to quit the comfort and civilisation of his home, to seek the perilous but engaging
life of a trapper of the Rocky Mountains.

La Bonté was raised in the state of Mississippi,
not far from Memphis, on the left bank of that
huge and snag-filled river. His father was a Saint
Louis Frenchman, his mother a native of Tennessee.
When a boy, our trapper was "some," he said,
with the rifle, and always had a hankering for the
west; particularly when, on accompanying his father
to Saint Louis every spring, he saw the different

bands of traders and hunters start upon their annual expeditions to the mountains. Greatly did he envy the independent, *insouciant* trappers, as, in all the glory of beads and buckskin, they shouldered their rifles at Jake Hawkin's door (the rifle-maker of St Louis), and bade adieu to the cares and trammels of civilised life.

However, like a thoughtless beaver-kitten, he put his foot into a trap one fine day, set by Mary Brand, a neighbour's daughter, and esteemed " some punkins," or in other words toasted as the beauty of Memphis County, by the susceptible Mississippians. From that moment he was " gone beaver ;" " he felt queer," he said, " all over, like a buffalo shot in the lights ; he had no relish for mush and molasses ; homminy and johnny cakes failed to excite his appetite. Deer and turkeys ran by him unscathed ; he didn't know, he said, whether his rifle had hind-sights or not. He felt bad, that was a fact ; but what ailed him he didn't know."

Mary Brand—Mary Brand—Mary Brand ! the old Dutch clock ticked it. Mary Brand ! his head throbbed it when he lay down to sleep. Mary Brand ! his rifle-lock spoke it plainly when he cocked it, to raise a shaking sight at a deer. Mary Brand, Mary Brand ! the whip-poor-will sung it, instead of her own well-known note ; the bull-frogs croaked it in the swamp, and mosquitoes droned it in his ear as he tossed about his bed at night, wakeful, and striving to think what ailed him.

Who could that strapping young fellow, who passed the door just now, be going to see? Mary Brand: Mary Brand. And who can Big Pete Herring be dressing that silver fox-skin so carefully for? For whom but Mary Brand? And who is it that jokes, and laughs, and dances, with all the " boys" but him; and why?

Who but Mary Brand : and because the love-sick booby carefully avoids her.

" And Mary Brand herself—what is she like?"

" She's ' some' now; that *is* a fact, and the biggest kind of punkin at that," would have been the answer from any man, woman, or child in Memphis County, and truly spoken too; always understanding that the pumpkin is the fruit by which the *ne-plus-ultra* of female perfection is expressed amongst the figuratively-speaking westerns.

Being an American woman, of course she was tall, and straight and slim as a hickory sapling, well formed withal, with rounded bust, and neck white and slender as the swan's. Her features were small, but finely chiselled ; and in this, it may be remarked, the lower orders of the American women differ from, and far surpass the same class in England, or elsewhere, where the features, although far prettier, are more vulgar and com-monplace. Mary Brand had the bright blue

eye, thin nose, and small but sweetly-formed
mouth, the too fair complexion and dark brown
hair, which characterise the beauty of the Anglo-
American, the heavy masses (hardly curls), that
fell over her face and neck, contrasting with their
polished whiteness. Such was Mary Brand : and
when to her good looks are added a sweet disposition,
and all the best qualities of a thrifty housewife, it
must be allowed that she fully justified the eulo-
giums of the good people of Memphis.

Well, to cut a love-story short, in doing which not
a little moral courage is shown, young La Bonté fell
desperately in love with the pretty Mary, and she
with him ; and small blame to her, for he was a
proper lad of twenty—six feet in his moccasins—
the best hunter and rifle-shot in the country, with
many other advantages too numerous to mention.
But when did the course, &c. e'er run smooth ?
When the affair had become a recognised " courting " (and Americans alone know the horrors of
such prolonged purgatory), they became, to use
La Bonté's words, " awful fond," and consequently
about once a-week had their tiffs and makes-up.

However, on one occasion, at a " husking," and
during one of these tiffs, Mary, every inch a woman,
to gratify some indescribable feeling, brought to
her aid jealousy—that old serpent who has caused
such mischief in this world ; and by a flirtation
over the corn-cobs with Big Pete, La Bonté's former and only rival, struck so hard a blow at the

latter's heart, that on the moment his brain caught
fire, blood danced before his eyes, and he became
like one possessed.   Pete observed and enjoyed his
struggling emotion—better for him had he minded
his corn-shelling alone ;—and the more to annoy
his rival, paid the most sedulous attention to pretty
Mary.

Young La Bonté stood it as long as human nature,
at boiling heat, could endure ; but when Pete, in
the exultation of his apparent triumph, crowned
his success by encircling the slender waist of the
girl with his arm, and snatching a sudden kiss, he
jumped upright from his seat, and seizing a small
whisky-keg which stood in the centre of the corn-
shellers, he hurled it at his rival, and crying to
him, hoarse with passion, " to follow if he was a
man," he left the house.

At that time, and even now, in the remoter states
of the western country, rifles settled even the most
trivial differences between the hot-blooded youths ;
and of such frequent occurrence and invariably
bloody termination did these encounters become,
that they scarcely produced sufficient excitement
to draw together half-a-dozen spectators.

In the present case, however, so public was the
quarrel, and so well known the parties concerned,
that not only the people who had witnessed the
affair, but all the neighbourhood, thronged to the
scene of action, in a large field in front of the
house, where the preliminaries of a duel between

Pete and La Bonté were being arranged by their respective friends.

Mary, when she discovered the mischief her thoughtlessness was likely to occasion, was almost beside herself with grief, but she knew how vain it would be to attempt to interfere. The poor girl, who was most ardently attached to La Bonté, was carried, swooning, into the house, where all the women congregated, and were locked in by old Brand, who, himself an old pioneer, thought but little of bloodshed, but refused to let the " women folk " witness the affray.

Preliminaries arranged, the combatants took up their respective positions at either end of a space marked for the purpose, at forty paces from each other. They were both armed with heavy rifles, and had the usual hunting-pouches, containing ammunition, hanging over the shoulder. Standing with the butts of their rifles on the ground, they confronted each other, and the crowd drawing away a few paces only on each side, left one man to give the word. This was the single word " fire ;" and, after this signal was given, the combatants were at liberty to fire away until one or the other dropped.

At the word, both the men quickly raised their rifles to the shoulder, and, whilst the sharp cracks instantaneously rang, they were seen to flinch, as either felt the pinging sensation of a bullet entering his flesh. Regarding each other steadily for a few

moments, the blood running down La Bonté's neck
from a wound under the left jaw, whilst his oppo-
nent was seen to place his hand once to his right
breast, as if to feel the position of his wound, they
commenced reloading their rifles.   But, as Pete was
in the act of forcing down the ball with his long
hickory wiping-stick, he suddenly dropped his right
arm—the rifle slipped from his grasp—and, reeling
for a moment like a drunken man—he fell dead to
the ground.

Even here, however, there was law of some kind
or another, and the consequences of the duel were,
that the constables were soon on the trail of La
Bonté to arrest him.   He easily avoided them, and
taking to the woods, lived for several days in as
wild a state as the beasts he hunted and killed for
his support.

Tired of this, he at last resolved to quit the country, and betake himself to the mountains, for which
life he had ever felt an inclination.

When, therefore, he thought the officers of justice had grown slack in their search of him, and
that the coast was comparatively clear, he determined to start on his distant expedition to the Far
West.

Once more, before he carried his project into
execution, he sought and obtained a last interview
with Mary Brand.

" Mary," said he, " I'm about to break. They're
hunting me like a fall buck, and I'm bound to quit.

Don't think any more about me, for I shall never come back."

Poor Mary burst into tears, and bent her head on the table near which she sat. When she again raised it, she saw La Bonté, his long rifle upon his shoulder, striding with rapid steps from the house. Year after year rolled on, and he did not return.

CHAPTER III.

A few days after his departure, La Bonté found himself at St Louis, the emporium of the fur trade, and the fast-rising metropolis of the precocious settlements of the west. Here, a prey to the agony of mind which jealousy, remorse, and blighted love mix into a very puchero of misery, he got into the company of certain " rowdies," a class that every western city particularly abounds in; and, anxious to drown his sorrows in any way, and quite unscrupulous as to the means, he plunged into all the vicious excitements of drinking, gambling, and fighting, which form the every-day amusements of the rising generation of St Louis.

Perhaps in no other part of the United States, where indeed humanity is frequently to be seen in many curious and unusual phases, is there a population so marked in its general character, and at the same time divided into such distinct classes, as in the above-named city. Dating, as it does, its foundation from yesterday—for what are thirty years in the growth of a metropolis?—its founders are now scarcely passed middle life, regarding with astonishment the growing works of their hands;

and whilst gazing upon its busy quays, piled with grain and other produce of the west, its fleets of huge steamboats lying tier upon tier alongside the wharves, its well-stored warehouses, and all the bustling concomitants of a great commercial depôt, they can scarcely realise the memory of a few short years, when on the same spot nothing was to be seen but the miserable hovels of a French village —the only sign of commerce being the unwieldy bateaux of the Indian traders, laden with peltries from the distant regions of the Platte and Upper Missouri. Where now intelligent and wealthy merchants walk erect, in conscious substantiality of purse and credit, and direct the commerce of a vast and well-peopled region, there stalked but the other day, in dress of buckskin, the Indian trader of the west ; and all the evidences of life, mayhap, consisted of the eccentric vagaries of the different bands of trappers and hardy mountaineers, who accompanied, some for pleasure and some as escort, the periodically arriving bateaux, laden with the beaver skins and buffalo robes collected during the season at the different trading posts in the Far West.

These, nevertheless, were the men whose hardy enterprise opened to commerce and the plough the vast and fertile regions of the West. Rough and savage though they were, they were the true pioneers of that extraordinary tide of civilisation which has poured its resistless current through tracts large

enough for kings to govern, over a country now
teeming with cultivation, where, a few short years
ago, countless herds of buffalo roamed unmolested,
where the bear and deer abounded, and the savage
Indian skulked through the woods and prairies,
lord of the unappreciated soil that now yields its
prolific treasures to the spade and plough of civilised man. To the wild and half-savage trapper,
who may be said to exemplify the energy, enterprise, and hardihood characteristic of the American
people, divested of all the false and vicious glare
with which a high state of civilisation, too rapidly
attained, has obscured their real and genuine character, in which the above traits are eminently prominent—to these men alone is due the empire of
the West—destined in a few short years to become
the most important of those confederate states com-
posing the mighty union of North America.

Sprung, then, out of the wild and adventurous
fur trade, St Louis, still the emporium of that species
of commerce, preserves even now, in the character
of its population, many of the marked peculiarities
distinguishing its early founders, who were identified
with the primitive Indian in hardihood and instinctive
wisdom.   Whilst the French portion of the population retain the thoughtless levity and frivolous disposition of their original source, the Americans of
St Louis, who may lay claim to be native, as it
were, are as strongly distinguished for determination and energy of character as they are for physical

strength and animal courage; and are remarkable,
at the same time, for a singular aptitude in carrying
out commercial enterprises to successful termina-
tions, apparently incompatible with the thirst of
adventure and excitement which forms so prominent
a feature in their character. In St Louis and with
her merchants have originated many commercial
enterprises of gigantic speculation, not confined to
the immediate locality or to the distant Indian fur
trade, but embracing all parts of the continent, and
even a portion of the Old World. And here it must
be remembered that St Louis is situated inland, at
a distance of upwards of one thousand miles from
the sea, and three thousand from the capital of the
United States.

Besides her merchants and upper class, who form
a little aristocracy even here, a large portion of her
population, still connected with the Indian and fur
trade, preserve all their original characteristics, un-
acted upon by the influence of advancing civilisation.
There is, moreover, a large floating population of
foreigners of all nations, who must possess no little
amount of enterprise to be tempted to this spot,
whence they spread over the remote western tracts,
still infested by the savage; so that, if any of their
blood is infused into the native population, the
characteristic energy and enterprise is increased,
and not tempered down by the foreign cross.

But perhaps the most singular of the casual population are the mountaineers, who, after several seasons

spent in trapping, and with good store of dollars,
arrive from the scene of their adventures, wild as
savages, determined to enjoy themselves, for a time,
in all the gaiety and dissipation of the western city.
In one of the back streets of the town is a tavern
well known as the "Rocky-Mountain House," and
hither the trappers resort, drinking and fighting
as long as their money lasts, which, as they are
generous and lavish as Jack Tars, is for a few days
only.. Such scenes, both tragic and comic, as are
enacted in the Rocky-Mountain House, are beyond
the powers of pen to describe; and when a fandango
is in progress, to which congregate the coquettish
belles from "Vide Poche," as the French portion of
the suburb is nicknamed,—the grotesque endeavours
of the bear-like mountaineers to sport a figure on
the light fantastic toe, and their insertions into the
dance of the mystic jumps of Terpsichorean Indians
when engaged in the "medicine" dances in honour
of bear, of buffalo, or ravished scalp,—are such
startling innovations on the choreographic art as
would make the shade of Gallini quake and gibber
in his pumps.

Passing the open doors and windows of the Mountain House, the stranger stops short as the sounds
of violin and banjo twang upon his ears, accompanied
by extraordinary noises—sounding unearthly to the
greenhorn listener, but recognised by the initiated
as an Indian song roared out of the stentorian lungs
of a mountaineer, who patting his stomach with

open hands, to improve the necessary shake, cho-
ruses the well-known Indian chant:—

> Hi—Hi—Hi—Hi,
> Hi-i—Hi-i—Hi-i—Hi-i
> Hi-ya—hi-ya—hi-ya—hi-ya
> Hi-ya—hi-ya—hi-ya—-hi-ya
> Hi-ya—hi-ya—hi—hi,
> &c. &c. &c.

and polishes off the high notes with a whoop which
makes the old wooden houses shake again, as it rattles and echoes down the street.

Here, over fiery "monaghahela," Jean Batiste,
the sallow half-breed voyageur from the north—
and who, deserting the service of the "North West"
(the Hudson's Bay Company), has come down the
Mississippi, from the "Falls," to try the sweets and
liberty of "free" trapping—hobnobs with a stalwart
leather-clad "boy," just returned from trapping on
the waters of Grand River, on the western side the
mountains, who interlards his mountain jargon with
Spanish words picked up in Taos and California.
In one corner a trapper, lean and gaunt from the
starving regions of the Yellow Stone, has just recognised an old companyero, with whom he hunted
years before in the perilous country of the Blackfeet.

"Why, John, old hos, how do you come on?"

"What! Meek, old 'coon! I thought you were
under?"

One from Arkansa stalks into the centre of the

room, with a pack of cards in his hand, and a handful of dollars in his hat. Squatting cross-legged on a buffalo robe, he smacks down the money, and cries out—" Ho, boys, hyar's a deck, and hyar's the beaver (rattling the coin), who dar set his hos? Wagh!"

Tough are the yarns of wondrous hunts and Indian perils, of hairbreadth 'scapes and curious " fixes." Transcendant are the qualities of sundry rifles, which call these hunters masters; " plum " is the " centre " each vaunted barrel shoots ; sufficing for a hundred wigs is the " hair " each hunter has " lifted " from Indians' scalps ; multitudinous the " coups" he has " struck." As they drink so do they brag, first of their guns, their horses, and their squaws, and lastly of themselves :—and when it comes to that, " ware steel."

La Bonté, on his arrival at St Louis, found himself one day in no less a place than this ; and here he made acquaintance with an old trapper about to start for the mountains in a few days, to hunt on the head waters of Platte and Green River. With this man he resolved to start, and, having still some hundred dollars in cash, he immediately set about equipping himself for the expedition. To effect this, he first of all visited the gun-store of Hawken, whose rifles are renowned in the mountains, and exchanged his own piece, which was of very small bore, for a regular mountain rifle. This was of very heavy metal, carrying about thirty-two balls to the pound, stocked to the muzzle, and mounted with brass, its only ornament being a buffalo bull, looking exceedingly ferocious, which was not very artistically engraved upon the trap in the stock. Here, too, he laid in a few pounds of powder and lead, and all the necessaries for a long hunt.

His next visit was to a smith's store, which smith was black by trade and black by nature, for he was a nigger, and, moreover, celebrated as being the best maker of beaver-traps in St Louis, and of him he purchased six new traps, paying for the same twenty dollars—procuring, at the same time, an old trap-sack, made of stout buffalo skin, in which to carry them.

We next find La Bonté and his companion—one Luke, better known as Grey-Eye, one of his eyes having been " gouged " in a mountain fray—at Independence, a little town situated on the Missouri, several hundred miles above St Louis, and within a short distance of the Indian frontier.

Independence may be termed the " prairie port " of the western country. Here the caravans destined for Santa Fé, and the interior of Mexico, assemble to complete their necessary equipment Mules and oxen are purchased, teamsters hired, and all stores and outfit laid in here for the long journey over the wide expanse of prairie ocean. Here, too, the Indian traders and the Rocky-Mountain trappers rendezvous, collecting in sufficient force to ensure their safe passage through the

Indian country. At the seasons of departure and
arrival of these bands, the little town presents a
lively scene of bustle and confusion. The wild and
dissipated mountaineers get rid of their last dollars
in furious orgies, treating all comers to galore of
drink, and pledging each other, in horns of potent
whisky, to successful hunts and " heaps of beaver."
When every cent has disappeared from their
pouches, the free trapper often makes away with
rifle, traps, and animals, to gratify his " dry " (for
your mountaineer is never " thirsty ") ; and then,
" hos and beaver" gone, is necessitated to hire
himself to one of the leaders of big bands, and
hypothecate his services for an equipment of traps
and animals. Thus La Bonté picked up three
excellent mules for a mere song, with their accompanying pack-saddles, *apishamores*,* and lariats,
and the next day, with Luke, " put out " for
Platte.

As they passed through the rendezvous, which
was encamped on a little stream beyond the town,
even our young Mississippian was struck with the
novelty of the scene. Upwards of forty huge
waggons, of Conostoga and Pittsburg build, and
covered with snow-white tilts, were ranged in a
semicircle, or rather a horse-shoe form, on the flat
open prairie, their long " tongues " (poles) pointing
outwards ; with the necessary harness for four

* Saddle-blanket made of buffalo-calf skin.

pairs of mules, or eight yoke of oxen, lying on
the ground beside them, spread in ready order for
" hitching up."   Round the waggons groups of
teamsters, tall stalwart young Missourians, were
engaged in busy preparation for the start, greasing
the wheels, fitting or repairing harness, smoothing
ox-bows, or overhauling their own moderate kits
or " possibles." They were all dressed in the same
fashion : a pair of " homespun" pantaloons, tucked
into thick boots reaching nearly to the knee, and
confined round the waist by a broad leathern belt,
which supported a strong butcher-knife in a sheath.
A coarse checked shirt was their only other covering, with a fur cap on the head.

Numerous camp-fires surrounded the waggons,
and near them lounged wild-looking mountaineers,
easily distinguished from the " greenhorn" teamsters by their dresses of buckskin, and their
weather-beaten faces.   Without an exception, these
were under the influence of the rosy god ; and one,
who sat, the picture of misery, at a fire by himself
—staring into the blaze with vacant countenance,
his long matted hair hanging in unkempt masses
over his face, begrimed with the dirt of a week,
and pallid with the effects of ardent drink—was
suffering from the usual consequences of having
" kept it up" beyond the usual point, paying the
penalty in a fit of " horrors"—as *delirium tremens*
is most aptly termed by sailors and the unpro-
fessional.

In another part, the merchants of the caravan and the Indian traders superintended the lading of the waggons, or mule packs. They were dressed in civilised attire, and some were even bedizened in St Louis or Eastern City dandyism, to the infinite disgust of the mountain men, who look upon a bourge-way (bourgeois) with most undisguised contempt, despising the very simplest forms of civilisation. The picturesque appearance of the encampment was not a little heightened by the addition of several Indians from the neighbouring Shawnee settlement, who, mounted on their small active horses, on which they reclined, rather than sat, in negligent attitudes, quietly looked on at the novel scene, indifferent to the " chaff " in which the thoughtless teamsters indulged at their expense. Numbers of mules and horses were picketed at hand, whilst a large herd of noble oxen were being driven towards the camp—the wo-ha of the teamsters sounding far and near, as they collected the scattered beasts in order to yoke up.

As most of the mountain men were utterly unable to move from camp, Luke and La Bonté, with three or four of the most sober, started in company, intending to wait on " Blue," a stream which runs into the Caw or Kanzas River, until the " balance " of the band came up. Mounting their mules, and leading the loose animals, they struck at once into the park-like prairie, and were speedily out of sight of civilisation.

It was the latter end of May, towards the close of the season of heavy rains, which in early spring render the climate of this country almost intolerable, at the same time that they fertilise and thaw the soil, so long bound up by the winter's frosts. The grass was every where luxuriantly green, and gaudy flowers dotted the surface of the prairie. This term, however, should hardly be applied to the beautiful undulating scenery of this park-like country. Unlike the flat monotony of the Grand Plains, here well wooded uplands, clothed with forest trees of every species, and picturesque dells, through which run clear bubbling streams belted with gay-blossomed shrubs, every where present themselves; whilst on the level meadow-land, topes of trees with spreading foliage afford a shelter to the game and cattle, and well-timbered knolls rise at intervals from the plain.

Many clear streams dashing over their pebbly beds intersect the country, from which, in the noonday's heat, the red-deer jump, shaking their wet sides, as the noise of approaching man disturbs them; and booming grouse rise from the tall luxuriant herbage at every step. Where the deep escarpments of the river banks exhibit the section of the earth, a rich alluvial soil of surpassing depth courts the cultivation of civilised man; and in every feature it is evident that here nature has worked with kindliest and most bountiful hand.

For hundreds of miles along the western or right

bank of the Missouri does a country extend, with
which, for fertility and natural resources, no part of
Europe can stand comparison. Sufficiently large
to contain an enormous population, it has, besides,
every advantage of position, and all the natural
capabilities which should make it the happy abode
of civilised man. Through this unpeopled country
the United States pours her greedy thousands, to
seize upon the barren territories of her feeble
neighbour.

Camping the first night on " Black Jack," our
mountaineers here cut each man a spare hickory
wiping-stick for his rifle; and La Bonté, who was
the only greenhorn of the party, witnessed a savage
ebullition of rage on the part of one of his companions, exhibiting the perfect unrestraint which these
men impose upon their passions, and the barbarous
anger which the slightest opposition to their will
excites. One of the trappers, on arriving at the
camping-place, dismounted from his horse, and,
after divesting it of the saddle, endeavoured to
lead his mule by the rope up to the spot where he
wished to deposit his pack. Mule-like, however,
the more he pulled the more stubbornly she
remained in her tracks, planting her fore-legs
firmly, and stretching out her neck with provoking obstinacy. Truth to tell, it does require
the temper of a thousand Jobs to manage a mule;
and in no case does the wilful mulishness of the
animal stir up one's choler more than in the very

trick this one played, and which is a daily occurrence. After tugging ineffectually for several
minutes, winding the rope round his body, and
throwing himself suddenly forward with all his
strength, the trapper actually foamed with passion;
and although he might have subdued the animal at
once by fastening the rope with a half-hitch round
its nose, this, with an obstinacy equal to that of the
mule itself, he refused to attempt, preferring to
vanquish her by main strength. Failing so to do,
the mountaineer, with a volley of blasphemous
imprecations, suddenly seized his rifle, and level-
ling it at the mule's head, shot her dead.

Passing the Wa-ka-rasha, a well-timbered
stream, they met a band of Osages going "to
buffalo." These Indians, in common with some
tribes of the Pawnees, shave the head, with the
exception of a ridge from the forehead to the
centre of the scalp, which is "roached" or hogged
like the mane of a mule, and stands erect, plastered
with unguents, and ornamented with feathers of
the hawk and turkey. The naked scalp is often
painted in mosaic with black and red, the face with
shining vermilion. This band were all naked to the
breech-clout, the warmth of the sun having made
them throw their dirty blankets from their shoulders. These Indians not unfrequently levy contributions on the strangers they accidentally meet;
but they easily distinguish the determined moun-

taineer from the incautious greenhorn, and think it
better to let the former alone.

Crossing Vermilion, the trappers arrived on the
fifth day at " Blue," where they encamped in the
broad timber belting the creek, and there awaited
the arrival of the remainder of the party.

It was two days before they came up; but the
following day they started for the mountains, fourteen in number, striking a trail which follows the
" Big Blue" in its course through the prairies,
which, as they advanced to the westward, gradually smoothed away into a vast unbroken expanse
of rolling plain. Herds of antelope began to show
themselves, and some of the hunters, leaving the
trail, soon returned with plenty of their tender
meat. The luxuriant but coarse grass they had
hitherto seen now changed into the nutritious and
curly buffalo grass, and their animals soon improved
in appearance on the excellent pasture. In a few
days, without any adventure, they struck the
Platte River, its shallow waters (from which it
derives its name) spreading over a wide and sandy
bed, numerous sand bars obstructing the sluggish
current, nowhere sufficiently deep to wet the for-
der's knee.

By this time, but few antelope having been seen,
the party ran entirely out of meat; and, one whole
day and part of another having passed without so
much as a stray rabbit presenting itself, not a few

objurgations on the buffalo grumbled from the lips
of the hunters, who expected ere this to have reached
the land of plenty. La Bonté killed a fine deer,
however, in the river bottom, after they had
encamped, not one particle of which remained after
supper that night, but which hardly took the rough
edge off their keen appetites. Although already in
the buffalo range, no traces of these animals had
yet been seen; and as the country afforded but little
game, and the party did not care to halt and lose
time in hunting for it, they moved along hungry and
sulky, the theme of conversation being the well
remembered merits of good buffalo meat,—of " fat
fleece," " hump rib," and " tender loin;" of delicious " boudins," and marrow bones too good to
think of. La Bonté had never seen the lordly animal, and consequently but half believed the accounts
of the mountaineers, who described their countless
bands as covering the prairie far as the eye could
reach, and requiring days of travel to pass through;
but the visions of such dainty and abundant feeding
as they descanted on set his mouth watering, and
danced before his eyes as he slept supperless, night
after night, on the banks of the hungry Platte.

One morning he had packed his animals before
the rest, and was riding a mile in advance of the
party, when he saw on one side the trail, looming
in the refracted glare which mirages the plains,
three large dark objects without shape or form,
which rose and fell in the exaggerated light like

F

ships at sea. Doubting what it could be, he approached the strange objects; and as the refraction disappeared before him, the dark masses assumed a more distinct form, and clearly moved with life. A little nearer, and he made them out—they were buffalo. Thinking to distinguish himself, the greenhorn dismounted from his mule, and quickly hobbled her, throwing his lasso on the ground to trail behind when he wished to catch her. Then, rifle in hand, he approached the huge animals, and, being a good hunter, knew well to take advantage of the inequalities of the ground and face the wind; by which means he crawled at length to within forty yards of the buffalo, which quietly cropped the grass, unconscious of danger. Now, for the first time, he gazed upon the noble beast he had so often heard of, and longed to see. With coal-black beard sweeping the ground as he fed, an enormous bull was in advance of the others, his wild brilliant eyes peering from an immense mass of shaggy hair, which covered his neck and shoulder. From this point his skin was smooth as one's hand, a sleek and shining dun, and his ribs were well covered with shaking flesh. Whilst leisurely cropping the short curly grass he occasionally lifted his tail into the air, and stamped his foot as a fly or musquito annoyed him—flapping the intruder with his tail, or snatching at the itching part with his ponderous head.

When La Bonté had sufficiently admired the buffalo, he lifted his rifle, and, taking steady aim, and certain of his mark, pulled the trigger, expecting to see the huge beast fall over at the report. What was his surprise and consternation, however, to see the animal only flinch when the ball struck him, and then gallop off, followed by the others, apparently unhurt. As is generally the case with greenhorns, he had fired too high, ignorant that the only certain spot to strike a buffalo is but a few inches above the brisket, and that a higher shot is rarely fatal. When he rose from the ground, he saw all the party halting in full view of his discomfiture; and when he joined them, loud were the laughs, and deep the regrets of the hungry at his first attempt.

However, they now knew that they were in the country of meat; and a few miles farther, another band of stragglers presenting themselves, three of the hunters went in pursuit, La Bonté taking a mule to pack in the meat. He soon saw them crawling towards the band, and shortly two puffs of smoke, and the sharp cracks of their rifles, showed that they had got within shot; and when he rode up, two fine buffaloes were stretched upon the ground. Now, for the first time, he was initiated in the mysteries of " butchering." He watched the hunters as they turned the carcass on the belly, stretching out the legs to support it on each side. A transverse cut was then made at the nape of the neck, and, gathering the long hair of the boss in one hand, the skin was separated from the shoulder. It was then laid

open from this point to the tail, along the spine, and
then, freed from the sides and pulled down to the
brisket, but still attached to it, was stretched upon
the ground to receive the dissected portions. Then
the shoulder was severed, the fleece removed from
along the backbone, and the hump-ribs cut off with
a tomahawk. All this was placed upon the skin;
and after the " boudins" had been withdrawn from
the stomach, and the tongue—a great dainty—taken
from the head, the meat was packed upon the mule,
and the whole party hurried to camp rejoicing.

There was merry-making in the camp that night,
and the way they indulged their appetites—or, in
their own language, " throw'd" the meat " cold"—
would have made the heart of a dyspeptic leap for
joy or burst with envy. Far into the " still watches
of the tranquil night" the fat-clad " depouille" saw
its fleshy mass grow small by degrees and beautifully less, before the trenchant blades of the hungry
mountaineers; appetising yards of well-browned
" boudin" slipped glibly down their throats; rib
after rib of tender hump was picked and flung to
the wolves; and when human nature, with helpless
gratitude, and confident that nothing of superexcel-
lent comestibility remained, was lazily wiping the
greasy knife that had done such good service,—a
skilful hunter was seen to chuckle to himself as he
raked the deep ashes of the fire, and drew there-
from a pair of tongues so admirably baked, so soft,
so sweet, and of such exquisite flavour, that a veil is

considerately drawn over the effects their discussion produced in the mind of our greenhorn La Bonté, and the raptures they excited in the bosom of that, as yet, most ignorant mountaineer. Still, as he ate he wondered, and wondering admired, that nature, in giving him such profound gastronomic powers, and such transcendant capabilities of digestion, had yet bountifully provided an edible so peculiarly adapted to his ostrich-like appetite, that after consuming nearly his own weight in rich and fat buffalo meat, he felt as easy and as little incommoded as if he had lightly supped on strawberries and cream.

Sweet was the digestive pipe after such a feast; soft was the sleep and deep, which sealed the eyes of the contented trappers that night. It felt like the old thing, they said, to be once more amongst the "meat;" and, as they were drawing near the dangerous portion of the trail, they felt at home; although they now could never be confident, when they lay down at night upon their buffalo robes, of awaking again in this life, knowing, as they did, full well, that savage men lurked near, thirsting for their blood.

However, no enemies showed themselves as yet, and they proceeded quietly up the river, vast herds of buffaloes darkening the plains around them, affording them more than abundance of the choicest meat; but, to their credit be it spoken, no more was killed than was absolutely required,—unlike the cruel slaughter made by most of the white travellers across the plains, who wantonly destroy these noble animals, not even for the excitement of sport, but in cold-blooded and insane butchery. La Bonté had practice enough to perfect him in the art, and, before the buffalo range was passed, he was ranked as a first-rate hunter. One evening he had left the camp for meat, and was approaching a band of cows for that purpose, crawling towards them along the bed of a dry hollow in the prairie, when he observed them suddenly jump towards him, and immediately afterwards a score of mounted Indians appeared, whom, by their dress, he at once knew to be Pawnees and enemies. Thinking they might not discover him, he crouched down in the ravine; but a noise behind caused him to turn his head, and he saw some five or six advancing up the bed of the dry creek, whilst several more were riding on the bluffs. The cunning savages had cut off his retreat to his mule, which he saw in the possession of one of them. His presence of mind, however, did not desert him; and seeing at once that to remain where he was would be like being caught in a trap (as the Indians could advance to the edge of the bluff and shoot him from above), he made for the open prairie, determined at least to sell his scalp dearly, and make " a good fight." With a yell the Indians charged, but halted when they saw the sturdy trapper deliberately kneel, and, resting his rifle on the wiping-stick, take a steady aim as they advanced. Full well the Pawnees know, to their cost, that a

mountaineer seldom pulls his trigger without sending a bullet to the mark; and, certain that one at
least must fall, they hesitated to make the onslaught.
Steadily the white retreated with his face to the foe,
bringing the rifle to his shoulder the instant that one
advanced within shot, the Indians galloping round,
firing the few guns they had amongst them at long
distances, but without effect. One young "brave,"
more daring than the rest, rode out of the crowd,
and dashed at the hunter, throwing himself, as he
passed within a few yards, from the saddle, and
hanging over the opposite side of his horse, thus
presenting no other mark than his left foot. As he
crossed La Bonté, he discharged his bow from under
his horse's neck, and with such good aim, that the
arrow, whizzing through the air, struck the stock
of the hunter's rifle, which was at his shoulder, and,
glancing off, pierced his arm, inflicting, luckily, but
a slight wound. Again the Indian turned in his
course, the others encouraging him with loud war-
whoops, and, once more passing at still less distance,
he drew his arrow to the head. This time, however, the eagle eye of the white detected the action,
and suddenly rising from his knee as the Indian
approached (hanging by his foot alone over the
opposite side of the horse), he jumped towards the
animal with outstretched arms and a loud yell,
causing it to start suddenly, and swerve from its
course. The Indian lost his foot-hold, and, after a
fruitless struggle to regain his position, fell to the

ground; but instantly rose upon his feet and gallantly confronted the mountaineer, striking his hand upon his brawny chest and shouting a loud whoop of defiance. In another instant the rifle of La Bonté had poured forth its contents; and the brave savage, springing into the air, fell dead to the ground, just as the other trappers, who had heard the firing, galloped up to the spot. At sight of them the Pawnees, with yells of disappointed vengeance, hastily retreated.

That night La Bonté first lifted hair!

A few days later the mountaineers reached the point where the Platte divides into two great forks: the northern one, stretching to the north-west, skirts the eastern base of the Black Hills, and sweeping round to the south rises in the vicinity of the mountain valley called the New Park, receiving the Laramie, Medicine Bow, and Sweet-Water creeks. The other, or " South Fork," strikes towards the mountains in a south-westerly direction, hugging the base of the main chain of the Rocky Mountains; and, fed by several small creeks, rises in the uplands of the Bayou Salade, near which is also the source of the Arkansa. To the forks of the Platte the valley of that river extends from three to five miles on each side, enclosed by steep sandy bluffs, from the summits of which the prairies stretch away in broad undulating expanse to the north and south. The " bottom," as it is termed, is but thinly covered with timber, the cotton-woods being scattered only here and there ; but some of the islands in the broad bed of the stream are well wooded, leading to the inference that the trees on the banks have been felled by Indians who formerly frequented the neighbourhood of this river as a chosen hunting-ground. As, during the long winters, the pasture in the vicinity is scarce and withered, the Indians feed their horses on the bark of the sweet cotton-wood, upon which they subsist, and even fatten. Thus, wherever a village has encamped, the trunks of these trees strew the ground, their upper limbs and smaller branches peeled of their bark, and looking as white and smooth as if scraped with a knife.

On the forks, however, the timber is heavier and of greater variety, some of the creeks being well wooded with ash and cherry, which break the monotony of the everlasting cotton-wood.

Dense masses of buffalo still continued to darken the plains, and numerous bands of wolves hovered round the outskirts of the vast herds, singling out the sick and wounded animals, and preying upon such calves as the rifles and arrows of the hunters had bereaved of their mothers. The white wolf is the invariable attendant upon the buffalo ; and when one of these persevering animals is seen, it is certain sign that buffalo are not far distant. Besides the buffalo wolf, there are four distinct varieties common to the plains, and all more or less attendant upon the buffalo. These are, the black, the

gray, the brown, and last and least the *coyote*, or
cayeute of the mountaineers, the " *wach-unka-
mănet,*" or " medicine wolf" of the Indians, who
hold the latter animal in reverential awe. This
little wolf, whose fur is of great thickness and
beauty, is of diminutive size, but wonderfully saga-
cious, making up by cunning what it wants in physical strength. In bands of from three to thirty
they not unfrequently station themselves along the
" runs" of the deer and the antelope, extending
their line for many miles—and the quarry being
started, each wolf follows in pursuit until tired,.
when it relinquishes the chase to another relay,
following slowly after until the animal is fairly run
down, when all hurry to the spot and speedily con-
sume the carcass. The cayeute, however, is often
made a tool of by his larger brethren, unless,
indeed, he acts from motives of spontaneous charity.
When a hunter has slaughtered game, and is in the
act of butchering it, these little wolves sit patiently
at a short distance from the scene of operations,
while at a more respectful one the larger wolves
(the white or gray) lope hungrily around, licking
their chops in hungry expectation. Not unfrequently the hunter throws a piece of meat towards
the smaller one, who seizes it immediately, and runs
off with the morsel in his mouth. Before he gets
many yards with his prize, the large wolf pounces
with a growl upon him, and the cayeute, dropping
the meat, returns to his former position, and will

continue his charitable act as long as the hunter
pleases to supply him.

Wolves are so common on the plains and in the
mountains, that the hunter never cares to throw
away a charge of ammunition upon them, although
the ravenous animals are a constant source of annoy-
ance to him, creeping to the camp-fire at night, and
gnawing his saddles and *apishamores*, eating the
skin ropes which secure the horses and mules to
their pickets, and even their very hobbles, and not
unfrequently killing or entirely disabling the animals themselves.

Round the camp, during the night, the cayeute
keeps unremitting watch, and the traveller not
unfrequently starts from his bed with affright, as
the mournful and unearthly chiding of the wolf
breaks suddenly upon his ear : the long-drawn
howl being taken up by others of the band, until it
dies away in the distance, or some straggler passing within hearing answers to the note, and howls
as he lopes away.

Our party crossed the south fork about ten miles
from its juncture with the main stream, and then,
passing the prairie, struck the north fork a day's
travel from the other. At the mouth of an ash-
timbered creek they came upon Indian " sign,"
and, as now they were in the vicinity of the treacherous Sioux, they moved along with additional
caution, Frapp and Gonneville, two experienced
mountaineers, always heading the advance.

About noon they had crossed over to the left bank of the fork, intending to camp on a large creek where some fresh beaver " sign " had attracted the attention of some of the trappers ; and as, on further examination, it appeared that two or three lodges of that animal were not far distant, it was determined to remain here a day or two, and set their traps.

Gonneville, old Luke, and La Bonté, had started up the creek, and were carefully examining the banks for " sign," when the former, who was in front, suddenly paused, and looking intently up the stream, held up his hand to his companions to signal them to stop.

Luke and La Bonté both followed the direction of the trapper's intent and fixed gaze. The former uttered in a suppressed tone the expressive exclamation, Wagh !—the latter saw nothing but a wood-duck swimming swiftly down the stream, followed by her downy progeny.

Gonneville turned his head, and extending his arm twice with a forward motion up the creek, whispered—" Les sauvages."

" Injuns, sure, and Sioux at that," answered Luke.

Still La Bonté looked, but nothing met his view but the duck with her brood, now rapidly approaching ; and as he gazed, the bird suddenly took wing, and, flapping on the water, flew a short distance down the stream and once more settled on it.

" Injuns ? " he asked; " where are they ? "

" Whar ? " repeated old Luke, striking the flint of his rifle, and opening the pan to examine the priming. " What brings a duck a-streakin it down stream, if humans aint behint her ? and who's thar in these diggins but Injuns, and the worst kind ? and we'd better push to camp, I'm thinking, if we mean to save our hair."

" Sign " sufficient, indeed, it was to all the trappers, who, on being apprised of it, instantly drove in their animals, and picketed them ; and hardly had they done so when a band of Indians made their appearance on the banks of the creek, from whence they galloped to the bluff which overlooked the camp at the distance of about six hundred yards; and crowning this, in number some forty or more, commenced brandishing their spears and guns, and whooping loud yells of defiance. The trappers had formed a little breast-work of their packs, forming a semicircle, the chord of which was made by the animals standing in a line, side by side, closely picketed and hobbled. Behind this defence stood the mountaineers, rifle in hand, and silent and determined. The Indians presently descended the bluff on foot, leaving their animals in charge of a few of the party, and, scattering, advanced under cover of the sage bushes which dotted the bottom, to about two hundred yards of the whites. Then a chief advanced before the rest, and made the sign for a talk with the Long-knives,

which led to a consultation amongst the latter, as
to the policy of acceding to it. They were in
doubts as to the nation these Indians belonged to,
some bands of the Sioux being friendly, and others
bitterly hostile to the whites.

Gonneville, who spoke the Sioux language, and
was well acquainted with the nation, affirmed they
belonged to a band called the Yanka-taus, well
known to be the most evil-disposed of that treacherous nation ; another of the party maintained they
were Brulés, and that the chief advancing towards
them was the well-known Tah-sha-tunga or Bull
Tail, a most friendly chief of that tribe.   The majo-
rity, however, trusted to Gonneville, and he volunteered to go out to meet the Indian, and hear what
he had to say.   Divesting himself of all arms save
his butcher-knife, he advanced towards the savage,
who awaited his approach, enveloped in the folds of
his blanket.   At a glance he knew him to be a
Yanka-tau, from the peculiar make of his moccasins, and the way in which his face was daubed with
paint.

" Howgh ! " exclaimed both as they met ; and,
after a silence of a few moments, the Indian spoke,
asking—" Why the Long-knives hid behind their
packs, when his band approached ? Were they
afraid, or were they preparing a dog-feast to enter-
tain their friends ? The whites were passing through
his country, burning his wood, drinking his water,
and killing his game ; but he knew they had now

come to pay for the mischief they had done, and that the mules and horses they had brought with them were intended as a present to their red friends.

" He was Mah-to-ga-shane," he said, " the Brave Bear : his tongue was short, but his arm long ; and he loved rather to speak with his bow and his lance than with the weapon of a squaw. He had said it : the Long-knives had horses with them and mules ; and these were for him, he knew, and for his ' braves.' Let the White-face go back to his people and return with the animals, or he, the ' Brave Bear,' would have to come and take them ; and his young men would get mad and would feel blood in their eyes ; and then he would have no power over them ; and the whites would have to ' go under.' "

The trapper answered shortly.—" The Long-knives," he said, " had brought the horses for themselves—their hearts were big, but not towards the Yanka-taus : and if they had to give up their animals, it would be to *men* and not *squaws.* They were not ' wah-keitcha,'* (French engagés), but Long-knives ; and, however short were the tongues of the Yanka-taus, theirs were still shorter, and their rifles longer. The Yanka-taus were dogs and squaws, and the Long-knives spat upon them."

Saying this, the trapper turned his back and

* The French Canadians are called *wah-keitcha*—" bad medicine "—by the Indians, who account them treacherous and vin-
dictive, and at the same time less daring than the American
hunters.

rejoined his companions; whilst the Indian slowly
proceeded to his people, who, on learning the con-
temptuous way in which their threats had been
treated, testified their anger with loud yells; and,
seeking whatever cover was afforded, commenced a
scattering volley upon the camp of the mountaineers. The latter reserved their fire, treating
with cool indifference the balls which began to
rattle about them; but as the Indians, emboldened
by this apparent inaction, rushed for a closer position, and exposed their bodies within a long range,
half-a-dozen rifles rang from the assailed, and two
Indians fell dead, one or two more being wounded.
As yet, not one of the whites had been touched,
but several of the animals had received wounds
from the enemy's fire of balls and arrows. Indeed,
the Indians remained at too great a distance to
render the volleys from their crazy fusees any thing
like effectual, and had to raise their pieces considerably to make their bullets reach as far as the camp.
After three of their band had been killed outright,
and many more wounded, their fire began to slack-
en, and they drew off to a greater distance, evidently
resolved to beat a retreat. Retiring to the bluff,
they discharged their pieces in a last volley, mounted their horses and galloped off, carrying their
wounded with them. This last volley, however,
although intended as a mere bravado, unfortunately
proved fatal to one of the whites. Gonneville, at
the moment, was standing on a pack, to get an un-

interrupted sight for a last shot, when one of the random bullets struck him in the breast. La Bonté caught him in his arms as he was about to fall, and laying the wounded trapper gently on the ground, stripped him of his buckskin hunting-frock, to examine the wound. A glance was sufficient to convince his companions that the blow was mortal. The ball had passed through the lungs; and in a few moments the throat of the wounded man swelled and turned to a livid blue colour, as the choking blood ascended. Only a few drops of purple blood trickled from the wound,—a fatal sign,—and the eyes of the mountaineer were already glazing with death's icy touch. His hand still grasped the barrel of his rifle, which had done good service in the fray. Anon he essayed to speak, but, choked with blood, only a few inarticulate words reached the ears of his companions, as they bent over him.

"Rubbed—out—at—last," they heard him say, the words gurgling in his blood-filled throat; and opening his eyes once more, and turning them upwards for a last look at the bright sun, the trapper turned gently on his side and breathed his last sigh.

With no other tools than their scalp-knives, the hunters dug a grave on the banks of the creek; and whilst some were engaged in this work, others sought the bodies of the Indians they had slain in the attack, and presently returned with three reeking scalps, the trophies of the fight. The body of

G

the mountaineer was wrapped in a buffalo robe, the
scalps being placed on his breast, and the dead man
was then laid in the shallow grave, and quickly
covered—without a word of prayer, or sigh of grief;
for, however much his companions may have felt,
not a word escaped them. The bitten lip and
frowning brow told of anger rather than of sorrow,
as they vowed—what they thought would better
please the spirit of the dead man than vain regrets
—bloody and lasting revenge.

Trampling down the earth which filled the grave,
they raised upon it a pile of heavy stones; and
packing their mules once more, and taking a last
look at their comrade's lonely resting-place, they
turned their backs upon the stream, which has ever
since been known as " Gonneville's Creek."

If the reader casts his eye over any of the recent
maps of the western country, which detail the features of the regions embracing the Rocky Mountains, and the vast prairies at their bases, he will
not fail to observe that many of the creeks or
smaller streams which feed the larger rivers,—as
the Missouri, Platte, and Arkansa,—are called by
familiar proper names, both English and French.
These are invariably christened after some unfortunate trapper, killed there in Indian fight; or
treacherously slaughtered by the lurking savages,
while engaged in trapping beaver on the stream.
Thus alone is the memory of these hardy men
perpetuated, at least of those whose fate is ascer-

tained : for many, in every season, never return
from their hunting expeditions, but meet a sudden
death from Indians, or a more lingering fate from
accident or disease in some lonely gorge of the
mountains, where no footfall save their own, or the
heavy tread of grizzly bear, disturbs the unbroken
silence of the awful solitude. Then, as many winters pass without some old familiar faces making
their appearance at the merry rendezvous, their
long protracted absence may perhaps elicit a remark, as to where such and such a mountain worthy
can have betaken himself, to which the casual rejoin-
der of " Gone under, maybe," too often gives a
short but certain answer.

In all the philosophy of hardened hearts, our
hunters turned from the spot where the unmourned
trapper met his death. La Bonté, however, not
yet entirely steeled by mountain life to a perfect
indifference to human feeling, drew his hard hand
across his eye, as the unbidden tear rose from his
rough but kindly heart. He could not forget so
soon the comrade he had lost, the companion in the
hunt or over the cheerful camp-fire, the narrator of
many a tale of dangers past, of sufferings from hunger, cold, thirst, and untended wounds, of Indian
perils, and other vicissitudes. One tear dropped
from the young hunter's eye, and rolled down his
cheek—the last for many a long year.

In the forks of the northern branch of the Platte,

formed by the junction of the Laramie, they found a big village of the Sioux encamped near the station of one of the fur companies.   Here the party broke up; many, finding the alcohol of the traders an impediment to their further progress, remained some time in the vicinity, while La Bonté, Luke, and a trapper named Marcelline, started in a few days to the mountains, to trap on Sweet Water and Medicine Bow.   They had leisure, however, to observe all the rascalities connected with the Indian trade, although at this season (August) hardly commenced. However, a band of Indians having come in with several packs of last year's robes, and being anxious to start speedily on their return, a trader from one of the forts had erected his lodge in the village.

Here he set to work immediately, to induce the Indians to trade.   First, a chief appoints three " soldiers" to guard the trader's lodge from intrusion; and these sentries amongst the thieving fraternity can be invariably trusted.   Then the Indians are invited to have a drink—a taste of the fire-water being given to all to incite them to trade. As the crowd presses upon the entrance to the lodge, and those in rear become impatient, some large-mouthed savage who has received a portion of the spirit, makes his way, with his mouth full of the liquor and cheeks distended, through the throng, and is instantly surrounded by his particular friends. Drawing the face of each, by turns, near his own, he squirts a small quantity into his open mouth, until the supply is exhausted, when he returns for more, and repeats the generous distribution.

When paying for the robes, the traders, in measuring out the liquor in a tin half-pint cup, thrust their thumbs or the four fingers of the hand into the measure, in order that it may contain the less, or not unfrequently fill the bottom with melted buffalo fat, with the same object. So greedy are the Indians, that they never discover the cheat, and, once under the influence of the liquor, cannot distinguish between the first cup of comparatively strong spirit, and the following ones diluted five hundred per cent, and poisonously drugged to boot.

Scenes of drunkenness, riot, and bloodshed last until the trade is over. In the winter it occupies several weeks, during which period the Indians present the appearance, under the demoralising influence of the liquor, of demons rather than of men.

CHAPTER IV.

LA BONTÉ and his companions proceeded up the
river, the Black Hills on their left hand, from
which several small creeks or feeders swell the
waters of the North Fork. Along these they
hunted unsuccessfully for beaver " sign," and it
was evident the spring hunt had almost extermi-
nated the animal in this vicinity. Following Deer
Creek to the ridge of the Black Hills, they crossed
the mountain on to the waters of the Medicine
Bow, and here they discovered a few lodges, and
La Bonté set his first trap. He and old Luke
finding " cuttings " near the camp, followed the
" sign " along the bank until the practised eye of
the latter discovered a " slide," where the beaver
had ascended the bank to chop the trunk of a
cotton wood, and convey the bark to its lodge.
Taking a trap from " sack," the old hunter, after
setting the trigger, placed it carefully under the
water, where the " slide " entered the stream, securing the chain to the stem of a sappling on the
bank ; while a stick, also attached to the trap by a
thong, floated down the stream, to mark the position of the trap, should the animal carry it away.

A little farther on, and near another " run," three traps were set ; and over these Luke placed a little stick, which he first dipped into a mysterious-looking phial containing his " medicine." *

The next morning they visited the traps, and had the satisfaction of finding three fine beaver secured in the first three they visited, and the fourth, which had been carried away, they discovered by the float-stick, a little distance down the stream, with a large drowned beaver between its teeth.

The animals being carefully skinned, they returned to camp with the choicest portions of the meat, and the tails, on which they most luxuriously supped ; and La Bonté was fain to confess that all his ideas of the superexcellence of buffalo were thrown in the shade by the delicious beaver tail, the rich meat of which he was compelled to allow was " great eating," unsurpassed by " tender loin " or " boudin," or other meat of whatever kind he had eaten of before.

The country where La Bonté and his companions were trapping, is very curiously situated in the extensive bend of the Platte which encloses the Black Hill range on the north, and which bounds the large expanse of broken tract known as the Laramie Plains, their southern limit being the base of the Medicine Bow Mountains. From the north-western corner of the bend, an inconsiderable range

* A substance obtained from a gland in the scrotum of the beaver, and used to attract that animal to the trap.

extends to the westward, gradually decreasing in
height until it reaches an elevated plain, which
forms a break in the stupendous chain of the Rocky
Mountains, and affords the easy passage now known
as the Great, or South Pass. So gradual is the
ascent of this portion of the mountain, that the
traveller can scarcely believe he is crossing the
dividing ridge between the waters which flow into
the Atlantic and Pacific Oceans, and that in a few
minutes he can fling two sticks into two neighbouring streams, one to be carried thousands of miles,
traversed by the eastern waters in their course to
the Gulf of Mexico, the other to be borne a lesser
distance to the Gulf of California.

The country is frequented by the Crows and
Snakes, who are at perpetual war with the Shians
and Sioux, following them often far down the Platte,
where many bloody battles have taken place.   The
Crows are esteemed friendly to the whites ; but
when on war expeditions, and " hair " their object,
it is always dangerous to fall in with Indian war-
parties, and particularly in the remote regions of
the mountains, where they do not anticipate retali-
ation.

Trapping with tolerable success in this vicinity,
the hunters crossed over, as soon as the premoni-
tory storms of approaching winter warned them to
leave the mountains, to the waters of Green River,
one of the affluents of the Colorado, intending to
winter at a rendezvous to be held in " Brown's

Hole"—an enclosed valley so called—which, abounding in game, and sheltered on every side by lofty mountains, is a favourite wintering-ground of the mountaineers. Here they found several trapping bands already arrived; and a trader from the Uintah country, with store of powder, lead, and tobacco, prepared to ease them of their hardly-earned peltries.

Singly, and in bands numbering from two to ten, the trappers dropped into the rendezvous; some with many pack-loads of beaver, others with greater or less quantity, and more than one on foot, having lost his animals and peltry by Indian thieving. Here were soon congregated many mountaineers, whose names are famous in the history of the Far West. Fitzpatrick and Hatcher, and old Bill Williams, well known leaders of trapping parties, soon arrived with their bands. Sublette came in with his men from Yellow Stone, and many of Wyeth's New Englanders were there. Chabonard with his half-breeds, Wah-keitchas all, brought his peltries from the lower country; and half-a-dozen Shawanee and Delaware Indians, with a Mexican from Taos, one Marcelline, a fine strapping fellow, the best trapper and hunter in the mountains, and ever first in the fight. Here, too, arrived the "Bourgeois" traders of the "North West"* Company, with their superior equipments, ready

* The Hudson's Bay Company is so called by the American trappers.

to meet their trappers, and purchase the beaver at an equitable value; and soon the trade opened, and the encampment assumed a busy appearance.

A curious assemblage did the rendezvous present, and representatives of many a land met there. A son of *La belle France* here lit his pipe from one proffered by a native of New Mexico. An Englishman and a Sandwich Islander cut a quid from the same plug of tobacco. A Swede and an " old Virginian" puffed together. A Shawanee blew a peaceful cloud with a scion of the " Six Nations." One from the Land of Cakes—a canny chiel— sought to " get round" (in trade) a right " smart " Yankee, but couldn't " shine."

The beaver went briskly, six dollars being the price paid per lb. in goods—for money is seldom given in the mountain market, where " beaver " is cash, for which the articles supplied by the traders are bartered. In a very short time peltries of every description had changed hands, either by trade, or by gambling with cards and betting. With the mountain men bets decide every question that is raised, even the most trivial; and if the Editor of *Bell's Life* were to pay one of these rendezvous a winter visit, he would find the broad sheet of his paper hardly capacious enough to answer all the questions which would be referred to his decision.

Before the winter was over, La Bonté had lost

all traces of civilised humanity, and might justly
claim to be considered as " hard a case " as any of
the mountaineers then present. Long before the
spring opened, he had lost all the produce of his
hunt and both his animals, which, however, by a
stroke of luck, he recovered, and wisely " held on
to " for the future. Right glad when spring appeared, he started from Brown's Hole, with four
companions, to hunt the Uintah or Snake country,
and the affluents of the larger streams which rise in
that region and fall into the Gulf of California.

In the valley of the Bear River they found
beaver abundant, and trapped their way westward
until they came upon the famed locality of the
Beer and Soda Springs—natural fountains of mineral water, renowned amongst the trappers as being
" medicine " of the first order.

Arriving one evening, about sun-down, at the
Bear Spring, they found a solitary trapper sitting
over the rocky basin, intently regarding, with no
little awe, the curious phenomenon of the bubbling
gas. Behind him were piled his saddles and a pack
of skins, and at a little distance a hobbled Indian
pony fed amongst the cedars which formed a grove
round the spring. As the three hunters dismounted
from their animals, the lone trapper scarcely noticed
their arrival, his eyes being still intently fixed upon
the water. Looking round at last, he was instantly
recognised by one of La Bonté's companions, and
saluted as " Old Rube." Dressed from head to foot

in buckskin, his face, neck, and hands appeared to
be of the same leathery texture, so nearly did they
assimilate in colour to the materials of his dress.
He was at least six feet two or three in his moccasins, straight-limbed and wiry, with long arms ending in hands of tremendous grasp, and a quantity
of straight black hair hanging on his shoulders.
His features, which were undeniably good, wore an
expression of comical gravity, never relaxing into
a smile, which a broad good-humoured mouth could
have grinned from ear to ear.

" What, boys," he said, " will you be simple
enough to camp here, alongside these springs?
Nothing good ever came of sleeping here, I tell
you, and the worst kind of devils are in those
dancing waters."

" Why, old hos," cried La Bonté, " what brings
you hyar then, and camp at that?"

" This niggur," answered Rube solemnly, " has
been down'd upon a sight too often to be skeared by
what can come out from them waters; and thar arn't
a devil as hisses thar, as can ' shine' with this child, I
tell you.   I've tried him onest, an' fout him to clawin'
away to Eustis,* and if I draws my knife again on
such varmint, I'll raise his hair, as sure as shootin.' "

Spite of the reputed dangers of the locality, the
trappers camped on the spot, and many a draught
of the delicious sparkling water they quaffed in

---

* A small lake near the head waters of the Yellow Stone,
near which are some curious thermal springs of ink-black water.

honour of the "medicine" of the fount. Rube,
however, sat sulky and silent, his huge form bending over his legs, which were crossed, Indian fashion,
under him, and his long bony fingers spread over
the fire, which had been made handy to the spring.
At last they elicited from him that he had sought
this spot for the purpose of "*making medicine*,"
having been persecuted by extraordinary ill luck,
even at this early period of his hunt—the Indians
having stolen two out of his three animals, and three
of his half-dozen traps. He had, therefore, sought
the springs for the purpose of invoking the foun-
tain spirits, which, a perfect Indian in his simple
heart, he implicitly believed to inhabit their mysterious waters. When the others had, as he thought,
fallen asleep, La Bonté observed the ill-starred
trapper take from his pouch a curiously carved red
stone pipe, which he carefully charged with tobacco
and kinnik-kinnik. Then approaching the spring,
he walked three times round it, and gravely sat
himself down. Striking fire with his flint and steel,
he lit his pipe, and, bending the stem three several
times towards the water, he inhaled a vast quantity
of smoke, and bending back his neck and looking
upwards, puffed it into the air. He then blew
another puff towards the four points of the compass,
and emptying the pipe into his hand, cast the con-
secrated contents into the spring, saying a few
Indian "medicine" words of cabalistic import.
Having performed the ceremony to his satisfaction,

he returned to the fire, smoked a pipe on his own hook, and turned into his buffalo robe, conscious of having done a most important duty.

In the course of their trapping expedition, and accompanied by Rube, who knew the country well, they passed near the Great Salt Lake, a vast inland sea, whose salitrose waters cover an extent of upwards of one hundred and forty miles in length, by eighty in breadth. Fed by several streams, of which the Big Bear River is the most considerable, this lake presents the curious phenomenon of a vast body of water without any known outlet. According to the trappers, an island, from which rises a chain of lofty mountains, nearly divides the north-western portion of the lake, whilst a smaller one, within twelve miles of the northern shore, rises six hundred feet from the level of the water. Rube declared to his companions that the larger island was known by the Indians to be inhabited by a race of giants, with whom no communication had ever been held by mortal man; and but for the casual wafting to the shores of the lake of logs of gigantic trees, cut by axes of extraordinary size, the world would never have known that such a people existed. They were, moreover, white as themselves, and lived upon corn and fruits, and rode on elephants, &c.

Whilst following a small creek at the south-west extremity of the lake, they came upon a band of miserable Indians, who, from the fact of their sub-

sisting chiefly on roots, are called the Diggers. At
first sight of the whites they immediately fled from
their wretched huts, and made towards the mountain ; but one of the trappers, galloping up on his
horse, cut off their retreat, and drove them like
sheep before him back to their village. A few of
these wretched creatures came into camp at sundown, and were regaled with such meat as the
larder afforded. They appeared to have no other
food in their village but bags of dried ants and
their larvæ, and a few roots of the yampah. Their
huts were constructed of a few bushes of grease-
wood, piled up as a sort of breakwind, in which
they huddled in their filthy skins. During the
night, they crawled up to the camp and stole two
of the horses, and the next morning not a sign of
them was visible. Now La Bonté witnessed a case
of mountain law, and the practical effects of the
" lex talionis " of the Far West.

The trail of the runaway Diggers bore to the
north-west, or along the skirt of a barren waterless
desert, which stretches far away from the southern
shores of the Salt Lake to the borders of Upper
California. La Bonté, with three others, determined to follow the thieves, recover their animals,
and then rejoin the other two (Luke and Rube) on
a creek two days' journey from their present camp.
Starting at sunrise, they rode on at a rapid pace all
day, closely following the trail, which led directly
to the north-west, through a wretched sandy coun-

try, without game or water. From the appearance of the track, the Indians must still have been seve-ral hours ahead of them, when the fatigue of their horses, suffering from want of grass and water, compelled them to camp near the head of a small water-course, where they luckily found a hole con-taining a little water, and whence a broad Indian trail passed, apparently frequently used. Long before daylight they were again in the saddle, and, after proceeding a few miles, saw the lights of seve-ral fires a short distance ahead of them. Halting here, one of the party advanced on foot to recon-noitre, and presently returned with the intelligence that the party they were in pursuit of had joined a village numbering thirty or forty huts.

Loosening their girths, they permitted their tired animals to feed on the scanty herbage which pre-sented itself, whilst they refreshed themselves with a pipe of tobacco—for they had no meat of any description with them, and the country afforded no game. As the first streak of dawn appeared in the east, they mounted their horses, after first examin-ing their rifles, and moved cautiously towards the Indian village. As it was scarcely light enough for their operations, they waited behind a sandhill in the vicinity, until objects became more distinct, and then, emerging from their cover with loud war-whoops, they charged abreast into the midst of the village.

As the frightened Indians were scarcely risen

from their beds, no opposition was given to the
daring mountaineers, who, rushing upon the flying
crowd, discharged their rifles at close quarters, and
then, springing from their horses, attacked them
knife in hand, and only ceased the work of butchery
when nine Indians lay dead upon the ground.
All this time the women, half dead with fright,
were huddled together on the ground, howling
piteously; and the mountaineers advancing to them,
whirled their lassos round their heads, and throwing the open nooses into the midst, hauled out
three of them, and securing their arms in the rope,
bound them to a tree, and then proceeded to scalp
the dead bodies. Whilst they were engaged in this
work, an old Indian, withered and grisly, and hardly
bigger than an ape, suddenly emerged from a rock,
holding in his left hand a bow and a handful of
arrows, whilst one was already drawn to the head.
Running towards them, and almost before the hunters were aware of his presence, he discharged an
arrow at a few yards' distance, which buried itself
in the ground not a foot from La Bonté's head as
he bent over the body of the Indian he was scalping; and hardly had the whiz ceased, when whirr
flew another, striking him in his right shoulder.
Before the Indian could fit a third arrow to his bow,
La Bonté sprang upon him, seized him by the middle, and spinning his pigmy form round his head,
as easily as he would have twirled a tomahawk, he
threw him with tremendous force on the ground at

H

the feet of one of his companions, who, stooping
down, coolly thrust his knife into the Indian's breast,
and quickly tore off his scalp.

The slaughter over, without casting an eye to the
captive squaws, the trappers proceeded to search
the village for food, of which they stood much in
need. Nothing, however, was found but a few bags
of dried ants, which, after eating voraciously of,
but with wry mouths, they threw aside, saying the
food was worse than " poor bull." They found,
however, the animals they had been robbed of, and
two more besides,—wretched half-starved creatures;
and on these mounting their captives, they hurried
away on their journey back to their companions,
the distance being computed at three days' travel
from their present position. However, they thought,
by taking a more direct course, they might find
better pasture for their animals, and water, besides
saving at least half a day by the short cut. To
their cost, they proved the old saying, that " a short
cut is always a long road," as will be presently
shown.

It has been said that from the south-western
extremity of the Great Salt Lake a vast desert
extends for hundreds of miles, unbroken by the
slightest vegetation, destitute of game and water,
and presenting a cheerless expanse of sandy plain,
or rugged mountain, thinly covered with dwarf pine
or cedar, the only evidence of vegetable life. Into
this desert, ignorant of the country, the trappers

struck, intending to make their short cut; and, travelling on all day, were compelled to camp at night, without water or pasture for their exhausted animals, and themselves ravenous with hunger and parched with thirst. The next day three of their animals " gave out," and they were fain to leave them behind; but imagining that they must soon strike a creek, they pushed on until noon, but still no water presented itself, nor a sign of game of any description. The animals were nearly exhausted, and a horse which could scarcely keep up with the slow pace of the others was killed, and its blood greedily drunk; a portion of the flesh being eaten raw, and a supply carried with them for future emergencies.

The next morning two of the horses lay dead at their pickets, and one only remained, and this in such a miserable state that it could not possibly have travelled six miles further. It was, therefore, killed, and its blood drunk, of which, however, the captive squaws refused to partake. The men began to feel the effects of their consuming thirst, which the hot horse's blood only served to increase; their lips became parched and swollen, their eyes blood-shot, and a giddy sickness seized them at intervals. About mid-day they came in sight of a mountain on their right hand, which appeared to be more thickly clothed with vegetation; and arguing from this that water would be found there, they left their course and made towards it, although some eight or ten

miles distant. On arriving at the base, the most
minute search failed to discover the slightest traces
of water, and the vegetation merely consisted of
dwarf piñon and cedar. With their sufferings increased by the exertions they had used in reaching
the mountain, they once more sought the trail, but
every step told on their exhausted frames. The
sun was very powerful, the sand over which they
floundered was deep and heavy, and, to complete
their sufferings a high wind blew it in their faces,
filling their mouths and noses with its searching par-
ticles.

Still they struggled onwards manfully, and not a
murmur was heard until their hunger had entered
the *second stage* upon the road to starvation. They
had now been three days without food or water;
under which privation nature can hardly sustain
herself for a much longer period. On the fourth
morning, the men looked wolfish, their captives following behind in sullen and perfect indifference,
occasionally stooping down to catch a beetle if one
presented itself, and greedily devouring it. A man
named Forey, a Canadian half-breed, was the first
to complain. " If this lasted another sundown," he
said, " some of them would ' be rubbed out;' that
meat had to be ' raised' anyhow; and for his part,
he knew where to look for a feed, if no game was
seen before they put out of camp on the morrow;
and meat was meat, anyhow they fixed it."

No answer was made to this, though his companions well understood him : their natures as yet revolted against the last expedient. As for the three squaws, all of them young girls, they followed behind their captors without a word of complaint, and with the stoical indifference to pain and suffering, which alike characterises the haughty Delaware of the north and the miserable stunted Digger of the deserts of the Far West. On the morning of the fifth day, the party were seated round a small fire of piñon, hardly able to rise and commence their journey, the squaws squatting over another at a little distance, when Forey commenced again to suggest that, if nothing offered, they must either take the alternative of starving to death, for they could not hope to last another day, or have recourse to the revolting extremity of sacrificing one of the party to save the lives of all. To this, however, there was a murmur of dissent, and it was finally resolved that all should sally out and hunt ; for a deer-track had been discovered near the camp, which, although it was not a fresh one, proved that there must be game in the vicinity. Weak and exhausted as they were, they took their rifles and started for the neighbouring uplands, each taking a different direction.

It was nearly sunset when La Bonté returned to the camp, where he already espied one of his companions engaged in cooking something over the fire. Hurrying to the spot, overjoyed with the anticipations of a feast, he observed that the squaws were gone; but, at the same time, thought it was not improbable they had escaped during their absence. Approaching the fire, he observed Forey broiling some meat on the embers, whilst at a little distance lay what he fancied was the carcass of a deer.

"Hurrah, boy!" he exclaimed, as he drew near the fire. "You've 'made' a 'raise,' I see."

"*Well*, I have," rejoined the other, turning his meat with the point of his butcher knife. "There's the meat, hos—help yourself."

La Bonté drew the knife from his scabbard, and approached the spot his companion was pointing to; but what was his horror to see the yet quivering body of one of the Indian squaws, with a large portion of the flesh butchered from it, part of which Forey was already greedily devouring. The knife dropped from his hand, and his heart rose to his throat.

The next day he and his companion struck the creek where Rube and the other trapper had agreed to await them, and found them in camp with plenty of meat, and about to start again on their hunt, having given up the others for lost. From the day they parted, nothing was ever heard of La Bonté's other two companions, who doubtless fell a prey to utter exhaustion, and were unable to return to the camp. And thus ended the Digger expedition.

It may appear almost incredible that men having civilised blood in their veins could perpetrate such wanton and cold-blooded acts of aggression on the wretched Indians, as that detailed above ; but it is fact that the mountaineers never lose an opportunity of slaughtering these miserable Diggers, and attacking their villages, often for the purpose of capturing women, whom they carry off, and not unfrequently sell to other tribes, or to each other. In these attacks neither sex nor age is spared; and your mountaineer has as little compunction in taking the life of an Indian woman, as he would have in sending his rifle-ball through the brain of a Crow or Blackfoot warrior.

La Bonté now found himself without animals, and fairly " afoot ;" consequently nothing remained for him but to seek some of the trapping bands, and hire himself for the hunt. Luckily for him, he soon fell in with Roubideau, on his way to Uintah, and was supplied by him with a couple of animals; and thus equipped, he started again with a large band of trappers, who were going to hunt on the waters of Grand River and the Gila. Here they fell in with another nation of Indians, from which branch out the innumerable tribes inhabiting Northern Mexico and part of California. They were in general friendly, but lost no opportunity of stealing horses or any articles left lying about the camp. On one occasion, the trappers being camped on a northern affluent of the Gila, a volley of arrows was discharged amongst them, severely wounding one or two of the party, as they sat round the camp fires. The attack, however, was not renewed,

and the next day the camp was moved further
down the stream, where beaver was tolerably
abundant. Before sundown a number of Indians
made their appearance, and making signs of peace,
were admitted into the camp.

The trappers were all sitting at their suppers
over the fires, the Indians looking gravely on,
when it was remarked that now would be a good
opportunity to retaliate upon them for the trouble
their incessant attacks had entailed upon the camp.
The suggestion was highly approved of, and
instantly acted upon. Springing to their feet, the
trappers seized their rifles, and commenced the
slaughter. The Indians, panic-struck, fled without
resistance, and numbers fell before the death-deal-
ing rifles of the mountaineers. A chief, who had
been sitting on a rock near the fire where the
leader of the trappers sat, had been singled out by
the latter as the first mark for his rifle.

Placing the muzzle to his heart, he pulled the
trigger, but the Indian, with extraordinary tena-
city of life, rose and grappled with his assailant.
The white was a tall powerful man, but, notwithstanding the deadly wound the Indian had received,
he had his equal in strength to contend against.
The naked form of the Indian twisted and writhed
in his grasp, as he sought to avoid the trapper's
uplifted knife. Many of the latter's companions
advanced to administer the *coup-de grâce* to the
savage, but the trapper cried to them to keep off :

" If he couldn't whip the Injun," he said, " he'd
go under."

At length he succeeded in throwing him, and,
plunging his knife no less than seven times into his
body, he tore off his scalp, and went in pursuit of
the flying savages. In the course of an hour or
two, all the party returned, and sitting by the
fires, resumed their suppers, which had been interrupted in the manner just described. Walker, the
captain of the band, sat down by the fire where he
had been engaged in the struggle with the Indian
chief, whose body was lying within a few paces of
it. He was in the act of fighting the battle over
again to one of his companions, and was saying
that the Indian had as much life in him as a buffalo
bull, when, to the horror of all present, the savage,
who had received wounds sufficient for twenty
deaths, suddenly rose to a sitting posture, the fire
shedding a glowing light upon the horrid spectacle.
The face was a mass of clotted blood, which flowed
from the lacerated scalp, whilst gouts of blood
streamed from eight gaping wounds in the naked
breast.

Slowly this frightful figure rose to a sitting posture, and, bending slowly forward to the fire, the
mouth was seen to open wide, and a hollow gurgling—owg-h-h—broke from it.

" H—!" exclaimed the trapper—and jumping
up, he placed a pistol to the ghastly head, the eyes
of which sternly fixed themselves on his, and pull-

ing the trigger, blew the poor wretch's skull to atoms.

The Gila passes through a barren, sandy country, with but little game, and sparsely inhabited by several different tribes of the great nation of the Apache. Unlike the rivers of this western region, this stream is, in most parts of its course, particularly towards its upper waters, entirely bare of timber, and the bottom, through which it runs, affords but little of the coarsest grass. Whilst on this stream, the trapping party lost several animals for want of pasture, and many more from the predatory attacks of the cunning Indians. These losses, however, they invariably made good whenever they encountered a native village—taking care, moreover, to repay themselves with interest whenever occasion offered.

Notwithstanding the sterile nature of the country, the trappers, during their passage up the Gila, saw with astonishment that the arid and barren valley had once been peopled by a race of men far superior to the present nomade tribes who roam over it. With no little awe they gazed upon the ruined walls of large cities, and the remains of houses, with their ponderous beams and joists, still testifying to the skill and industry with which they were constructed : huge ditches and irrigating canals, now filled with rank vegetation, furrowed the plains in the vicinity, marking the spot where once green waving maize and smiling gardens

covered what now is a bare and sandy desert.
Pieces of broken pottery, of domestic utensils,
stained with bright colours, every where strewed
the ground; and spear and arrow-heads of stone,
and quaintly carved idols, and women's ornaments
of agate and obsidian, were picked up often by the
wondering trappers, examined with child-like curiosity, and thrown carelessly aside.*

A Taos Indian, who was amongst the band, was
evidently impressed with a melancholy awe, as he
regarded these ancient monuments of his fallen
people. At midnight he rose from his blanket and
left the camp, which was in the vicinity of the
ruined city, stealthily picking his way through the
line of slumbering forms which lay around; and
the watchful sentinel observed him approach the
ruins with a slow and reverential gait. Entering
the mouldering walls, he gazed silently around,
where in ages past his ancestors trod proudly, a
civilised race, the tradition of which, well known to
his people, served but to make their present degraded position more galling and apparent. Cowering
under the shadow of a crumbling wall, the Indian
drew his blanket over his head, and conjured to his
mind's eye the former power and grandeur of his
race—that warlike people who, forsaking their own

* The Aztecs are supposed to have built this city during their
migration to the south; there is little doubt, however, but that
the region extending from the Gila to the Great Salt Lake, and
embracing the province of New Mexico, was the locality from
which they emigrated.

country for causes of which no tradition, however
dim, now exists, sought in the fruitful and teeming
valleys of the south a soil and climate which their
own lands did not afford; and, displacing the wild
and barbarous hordes inhabiting the land, raised
there a mighty empire, great in riches and civilisation.

The Indian bowed his head, and mourned the
fallen greatness of his tribe. Rising, he slowly
drew his tattered blanket round his body, and prepared to leave the spot, when the shadow of a
moving figure, creeping past a gap in the ruined
wall, through which the moonbeams played, suddenly arrested his attention. Rigid as a statue,
he stood transfixed to the spot, thinking a former
inhabitant of the city was visiting, in a ghostly
form, the scenes his body once knew so well. The
bow in his right hand shook with fear as he saw
the shadow approach, but was as tightly and
steadily grasped when, on the figure emerging
from the shade of the wall, he distinguished the
form of a naked Apache, armed with bow and
arrow, crawling stealthily through the gloomy
ruins.

Standing undiscovered within the shadow of the
wall, the Taos raised his bow, and drew an arrow
to the head, until the other, who was bending low
to keep under cover of the wall, and thus approach
the sentinel standing at a short distance, seeing
suddenly the well-defined shadow on the ground,

rose upright on his legs, and, knowing escape was impossible, threw his arms down his sides, and, drawing himself erect, exclaimed, in a suppressed tone, " Wa-g-h !"

" Wagh !" exclaimed the Taos likewise, but quickly dropped his arrow point, and eased the bow.

" What does my brother want," he asked, " that he lopes like a wolf round the fires of the white hunters ?"

" Is my brother's skin not red ?" returned the Apache, " and yet he asks a question that needs no answer. Why does the ' medicine wolf' follow the buffalo and deer ? For blood—and for blood the Indian follows the treacherous white from camp to camp, to strike blow for blow, until the deaths of those so basely killed are fully avenged."

" My brother speaks with a big heart, and his words are true; and though the Taos and Pimo (Apache) black their faces towards each other (are at war), here, on the graves of their common fathers, there is peace between them. Let my brother go."

The Apache moved quickly away, and the Taos once more sought the camp-fires of his white companions.

Following the course of the Gila to the eastward, they crossed a range of the Sierra Madre, which is a continuation of the Rocky Mountains, and struck the waters of the Rio del Norte, below the settle-

ments of New Mexico. On this stream they fared
well; besides trapping a great quantity of beaver,
game of all kinds abounded, and the bluffs near the
well-timbered banks of the river were covered with
rich gramma grass, on which their half-starved animals speedily improved in condition.

They remained for some weeks encamped on the
right bank of the stream, during which period they
lost one of their number, shot with an arrow whilst
lying asleep within a few feet of the camp-fire.

The Navajos continually prowl along that portion
of the river which runs through the settlements of
New Mexico, preying upon the cowardly inhabitants, and running off with their cattle whenever they
are exposed in sufficient numbers to tempt them.
Whilst ascending the river, the trappers met a party
of these Indians returning to their mountain homes
with a large band of mules and horses which they
had taken from one of the Mexican towns, besides
several women and children, whom they had captured, as slaves. The main body of the trappers
halting, ten of the band followed and charged upon
the Indians, who numbered at least sixty, killed
seven of them, and retook the prisoners and the
whole cavallada of horses and mules. Great were
the rejoicings when they entered Socorro, the town
whence the women and children had been taken,
and as loud the remonstrances, when, handing them
over to their families, the trappers rode on, driving
fifty of the best of the rescued animals before them,

which they retained as payment for their services. Messengers were sent on to Albuquerque with intelligence of the proceeding; and as troops were stationed there, the commandant was applied to, to chastise the insolent whites.

That warrior, on learning that the trappers numbered less than fifteen, became alarmingly brave, and ordering out the whole of his disposable force, some two hundred dragoons, sallied out to intercept the audacious mountaineers. About noon one day, just as the latter had emerged from a little town between Socorro and Albuquerque, they descried the imposing force of the dragoons winding along a plain ahead. As the trappers advanced, the officer in command halted his men, and sent out a trumpeter to order the former to await his coming. Treating the herald to a roar of laughter, on they went, and, as they approached the soldiers, broke into a trot, ten of the number forming line in front of the packed and loose animals, and, rifle in hand, charging with loud whoops. This was enough for the New Mexicans. Before the enemy were within shooting distance, the gallant fellows turned tail, and splashed into the river, dragging themselves up the opposite bank like half-drowned rats, and saluted with loud peels of laughter by the victorious mountaineers, who, firing a volley into the air, in token of supreme contempt, quietly continued their route up the stream.

Before reaching the capital of the province, they

struck again to the westward, and following a
small creek to its junction with the Green River,
ascended that stream, trapping *en route* to the
Uintah or Snake Fork, and arrived at Roubideau's
rendezvous early in the fall, where they quickly
disposed of their peltries, and were once more on
" the loose."

Here La Bonté married a Snake squaw, with
whom he crossed the mountains and proceeded to
the Platte through the Bayou Salade, where he
purchased of the Yutas a commodious lodge, with
the necessary poles, &c.; and being now " rich" in
mules and horses, and in all things necessary for
otium cum dignitate, he took unto himself another
wife, as by mountain law allowed; and thus equipped, with both his better halves attired in all the
glory of fofarraw, he went his way rejoicing.

In a snug little valley lying under the shadow of
the mountains, watered by Vermilion Creek, and
in which abundance of buffalo, elk, deer, and antelope fed and fattened on the rich grass, La Bonté
raised his lodge, employing himself in hunting, and
fully occupying his wives' time in dressing the skins
of the many animals he killed. Here he enjoyed
himself amazingly until the commencement of winter, when he determined to cross to the North Fork
and trade his skins, of which he had now as many
packs as his animals could carry. It happened that
he one day left his camp, to spend a couple of days
hunting buffalo in the mountains, whither the bulls

were now resorting, intending to "put out" for
Platte on his return. His hunt, however, led him
farther into the mountains than he anticipated, and
it was only on the third day that sundown saw him
enter the little valley where his camp was situated.

Crossing the creek, he was not a little disturbed
at seeing fresh Indian sign on the opposite side,
which led in the direction of his lodge; and his
worst fears were realised when, on coming within
sight of the little plateau where the conical top of
his white lodge had always before met his view, he
saw nothing but a blackened mass strewing the
ground, and the burnt ends of the poles which had
once supported it.

Squaws, animals, and peltry, all were gone—an
Arapaho moccasin lying on the ground told him
where. He neither fumed nor fretted, but, throwing
the meat off his pack animal, and the saddle from
his horse, he collected the blackened ends of the
lodge poles and made a fire—led his beasts to water
and hobbled them, threw a piece of buffalo meat
upon the coals, squatted down before the fire, and
lit his pipe. La Bonté was a true philosopher. Notwithstanding that his house, his squaws, his peltries,
were gone " at one fell swoop," the loss scarcely disturbed his equanimity; and before the tobacco in
his pipe was half smoked out, he had ceased to think
of his misfortune. Certes, as he turned his apolla
of tender loin, he sighed as he thought of the delicate manipulations with which his Shoshone squaw,

I

Sah-qua-manish, was wont to beat to tenderness the toughest bull meat—and missed the tending care of Yute Chil-co-thē, or the " reed that bends," in patching the holes worn in his neatly fitting moccasins, the work of her nimble fingers.   However, he ate and smoked, and smoked and ate, and slept none the worse for his mishap; thought, before he closed his eyes, a little of his lost wives, and more perhaps of the " Bending Reed" than of Sah-qua-manish, or " she who runs with the stream," drew his blanket tightly round him, felt his rifle handy to his grasp, and was speedily asleep.

Whilst the tired mountaineer breathes heavily in his dream, careless and unconscious that a living soul is near, his mule on a sudden pricks her ears and stares into the gloom, whence a figure soon emerges, and with noiseless steps draws near the sleeping hunter.   Taking one look at the slumbering form, the same figure approaches the fire and adds a log to the pile; which done, it quietly seats itself at the feet of the sleeper, and remains motionless as a statue.   Towards morning the hunter awoke, and, rubbing his eyes, was astonished to feel the glowing warmth of the fire striking on his naked feet, which, in Indian fashion, were stretched towards it; as by this time, he knew, the fire he left burning must long since have expired.   Lazily raising himself on his elbow, he saw a figure sitting near it with the back turned to him, which, although his exclamatory wagh was loud enough in all conscience, remained perfectly motionless, until the trapper, rising, placed his hand upon the shoulder : then, turning up its face, the features displayed to his wondering eye were those of Chil-co-thē, his Yuta wife. Yes, indeed, the " reed that bends" had escaped from her Arapaho captors, and made her way back to her white husband, fasting and alone.

The Indian women who follow the fortunes of the white hunters are remarkable for their affection and fidelity to their husbands, the which virtues, it must be remarked, are all on their own side ; for, with very few exceptions, the mountaineers seldom scruple to abandon their Indian wives, whenever the fancy takes them to change their harems ; and on such occasions the squaws, thus cast aside, wild with jealousy and despair, have been not unfrequently known to take signal vengeance both on their faithless husbands and on the successful beauties who have supplanted them in their affections. There are some honourable exceptions, however, to such cruelty, and many of the mountaineers stick to their red-skinned wives for better and for worse, often suffering them to gain the upper hand in the domestic economy of the lodges, and being ruled by their better halves in all things pertaining to family affairs ; and it may be remarked, that, when once the lady dons the unmentionables, she becomes the veriest termagant that ever henpecked an unfortunate husband.

Your refined trappers, however, who, after many

years of bachelor life, incline to take to themselves a
better half, often undertake an expedition into the
settlements of New Mexico, where not unfrequently
they adopt a very "Young Lochinvar" system in
procuring the required rib; and have been known
to carry off, *vi et armis*, from the midst of a fandango in Fernandez, or El Rancho of Taos, some
dark-skinned beauty—with or without her own consent is a matter of unconcern—and bear the ravished
fair one across the mountains, where she soon becomes inured to the free and roving life fate has
assigned her.

American women are valued at a low figure in
the mountains. They are too fine and "fofarraw."
Neither can they make moccasins, or dress skins;
nor are they so schooled to perfect obedience to
their lords and masters as to stand a "lodge-pole-
ing," which the western lords of the creation not
unfrequently deem it their bounden duty to inflict
upon their squaws for some dereliction of domestic
duty.

To return, however, to La Bonté. That worthy
thought himself a lucky man to have lost but one
of his wives, and she the worst of the two. "Here's
the beauty," he philosophised, "of having two
'wiping-sticks' to your rifle; if one breaks whilst
ramming down a ball, there's still hickory left to
supply its place." Although, with animals and
peltry, he had lost several hundred dollars' worth
of "possibles," he never groaned or grumbled.

" There's redskin will pay for this," he once muttered, and was done.

Packing all that was left on the mule, and mounting Chil-co-thē on his buffalo horse, he shouldered his rifle and struck the Indian trail for Platte. On Horse Creek they came upon a party of French * trappers and hunters, who were encamped with their lodges and Indian squaws, and formed quite a village. Several old companions were amongst them ; and, to celebrate the arrival of a " camarade," a splendid dog-feast was prepared in honour of the event. To effect this, the squaws sallied out of their lodges to seize upon sundry of the younger and plumper of the pack, to fill the kettles for the approaching feast. With a presentiment of the fate in store for them, the curs slunk away with tails between their legs, and declined the pressing invitations of the anxious squaws. These shouldered their tomahawks and gave chase ; but the cunning pups outstripped them, and would have fairly beaten the kettles, if some of the mountaineers had not stepped out with their rifles and quickly laid half-a-dozen ready to the knife. A cayeute, attracted by the scent of blood, drew near, unwitting of the canine feast in progress, and was likewise soon made *dog* of, and thrust into the boiling kettle with the rest.

The feast that night was long protracted ; and

* Creoles of St Louis, and French Canadians.

so savoury was the stew, and so agreeable to the palates of the hungry hunters, that at the moment the last morsel was drawn from the pot, when all were regretting that a few more dogs had not been slaughtered, a wolfish-looking cur, who incautiously poked his long nose and head under the lodge skin, was pounced upon by the nearest hunter, who in a moment drew his knife across the animal's throat, and threw it to a squaw to skin and prepare for the pot. The wolf had long since been vigorously discussed, and voted by all hands to be " good as dog."

" Meat's meat," is a common saying in the mountains, and from the buffalo down to the rattlesnake, including every quadruped that runs, every fowl that flies, and every reptile that creeps, nothing comes amiss to the mountaineer. Throwing aside all the qualms and conscientious scruples of a fastidious stomach, it must be confessed that *dog-meat* takes a high rank in the wonderful variety of cuisine afforded to the gourmand and the gourmet by the prolific " mountains." Now, when the bill of fare offers such tempting viands as buffalo beef, venison, mountain mutton, turkey, grouse, wildfowl, hares, rabbits, beaver and their tails, &c. &c., the station assigned to " dog " as No. 2 in the list can be well appreciated—No. 1, in delicacy of flavour, richness of meat, and other good qualities, being the flesh of *panthers*, which surpasses every other, and all put together.

" Painter meat can't ' shine ' with this," says a

hunter, to express the delicious flavour of an extra-ordinary cut of " tender loin," or delicate fleece.

La Bonté started with his squaw for the North Fork early in November, and arrived at the Laramie at the moment that the big village of the Sioux came up for their winter trade. Two other villages were encamped lower down the Platte, including the Brulés and the Yanka-taus, who were now on more friendly terms with the whites. The first band numbered several hundred lodges, and presented quite an imposing appearance, the village being laid out in parallel lines, the lodge of each chief being marked with his particular totem. The traders had a particular portion of the village allotted to them, and a line was marked out which was strictly kept by the soldiers appointed for the protection of the whites. As there were many rival traders, and numerous *coureurs des bois,* or peddling ones, the market promised to be brisk, the more so as a large quantity of ardent spirits was in their possession, which would be dealt with no unsparing hand to put down the opposition of so many competing traders.

In opening a trade a quantity of liquor is first given " on the prairie," * as the Indians express it in words, or by signs in rubbing the palm of one hand quickly across the other, holding both flat. Having once tasted the pernicious liquid, there is

---

* " On the prairie," is the Indian term for a free gift.

no fear but they will quickly come to terms ; and
not unfrequently the spirit is drugged, to render
the unfortunate Indians still more helpless. Sometimes, maddened and infuriated by drink, they
commit the most horrid atrocities on each other,
murdering and mutilating in a barbarous manner,
and often attempting the lives of the traders themselves. On one occasion a band of Sioux, whilst
under the influence of liquor, attacked and took
possession of a trading fort of the American Fur
Company, stripping it of every thing it contained,
and roasting the trader himself over his own fire.

The principle on which the nefarious trade is
conducted is this, that the Indians, possessing a
certain quantity of buffalo robes, have to be cheated
out of them, and the sooner the better. Although
it is explicitly prohibited by the laws of the United
States to convey spirits across the Indian frontier,
and its introduction amongst the Indian tribes subjects the offender to a heavy penalty ; yet the
infraction of this law is of daily occurrence, perpe-
trated almost in the very presence of the government officers, who are stationed along the frontier
for the purpose of enforcing the laws for the protection of the Indians.

The misery entailed upon these unhappy people
by the illicit traffic must be seen to be fully appreciated. Before the effects of the poisonous " fire-
water," they disappear from the earth like " snow
before the sun." Although aware of the destruc-

tion it entails upon them, the poor wretches have
not moral courage to shun the fatal allurement it
holds out to them, of wild excitement and a temporary oblivion of their many sufferings and privations.   With such palpable effects, it appears only
likely that the illegal trade is connived at by those
whose policy it has ever been, gradually but surely,
to exterminate the Indians, and by any means to
extinguish their title to the few lands they now
own on the outskirts of civilisation.   Certain it
it is that large quantities of liquor find their way
annually into the Indian country, and as certain
are the fatal results of the pernicious system, and
that the American government takes no steps to
prevent it.   There are some tribes who have as
yet withstood the great temptation, and have reso-
lutely refused to permit liquor to be brought into
their villages.   The marked difference between the
improved condition of these, and the moral and
physical abasement of those which give way to the
fatal passion for drinking, sufficiently proves the
pernicious effects of the liquor trade on the unfortunate and abused aborigines ; and it is matter of
regret that no philanthropist has sprung up in the
United States to do battle for the rights of the Red
men, and call attention to the wrongs they endure
at the hands of their supplanters in the lands of
their fathers.

Robbed of their homes and hunting-grounds, and
driven by the encroachments of the whites to dis-

tant regions, which hardly support existence, the Indians, day by day, gradually decrease before the accumulating evils, of body and soul, which their civilised persecutors entail upon them. With every man's hand against them, they drag on to their final destiny; and the day is not far distant when the American Indian will exist only in the traditions of his pale-faced conquerors.

The Indians trading at this time on the Platte were mostly of the Sioux nation, including the tribes of Burnt-woods, Yanka-taus, Pian-Kashas, Assinaboins, Oglallahs, Broken Arrows, all of which belong to the great Sioux nation, or La-cotahs, as they call themselves, and which means cut-throats. There were also some Cheyennes allied to the Sioux, as well as a small band of Republican Pawnees.

Horse-racing, gambling, and ball-play, served to pass away the time until the trade commenced, and many packs of dressed robes changed hands amongst themselves. When playing at the usual game of " *hand*," the stakes, comprising all the valuables the players possess, are piled in two heaps close at hand, the winner at the conclusion of the game sweeping the goods towards him, and often returning a small portion " on the prairie," with which the loser may again commence operations with another player.

The game of " hand " is played by two persons. One, who commences, places a plum or cherry-stone

in the hollow formed by joining the concaved palms
of the hands together, then shaking the stone for a
few moments, the hands are suddenly separated,
and the other player must guess which hand now
contains the stone.

Large bets are often wagered on the result of
this favourite game, which is also often played by
the squaws, the men standing round encouraging
them to bet, and laughing loudly at their grotesque
excitement.

A Burnt-wood Sioux, Tah-tunganisha, one of the
bravest chiefs of his tribe, was out, when a young
man, on a solitary war expedition against the
Crows. One evening he drew near a certain
" medicine " spring, where, to his astonishment, he
encountered a Crow warrior in the act of quenching
his thirst. He was on the point of drawing his
bow upon him, when he remembered the sacred
nature of the spot, and making the sign of peace,
he fearlessly drew near his foe, and proceeded likewise to slake his thirst. A pipe of kinnik-kinnik
being produced, it was proposed to pass away the
early part of the night in a game of " hand."
They accordingly sat down beside the spring, and
commenced the game.

Fortune favoured the Crow. He won arrow after
arrow from the Burnt-wood brave ; then his bow,
his club, his knife, his robe, all followed, and the
Sioux sat naked on the plain. Still he proposed
another stake against the other's winnings—his

scalp.   He played, and lost; and bending forward
his head, the Crow warrior drew his knife and
quickly removed the bleeding prize.   Without a
murmur the luckless Sioux rose to depart, but
first exacted a promise from his antagonist that he
would meet him once more at the same spot, and
engage in another trial of skill.

On the day appointed, the Burnt-wood sought
the spot, with a new equipment, and again the
Crow made his appearance, and they sat down to
play.   This time fortune changed sides; the Sioux
won back his former losses, and in his turn the
Crow was stripped to his skin.

Scalp against scalp was now the stake, and this
time the Crow submitted his head to the victorious
Burnt-wood's knife; and both the warriors stood
scalpless on the plain.

And now the Crow had but one single stake of
value to offer, and the offer of it he did not hesitate
to make.   He staked his life against the other's
winnings.   They played; and fortune still being
adverse, he lost.   He offered his breast to his
adversary.   The Burnt-wood plunged his knife
into his heart to the very hilt; and, laden with
his spoils, returned to his village, and to this day
wears suspended from his ears his own and enemy's
scalp.

The village presented the usual scene of confusion as long as the trade lasted.   Fighting, brawl-
ing, yelling, dancing, and all the concomitants of

intoxication, continued to the last drop of the
liquor-keg, when the reaction after such excitement was almost worse than the evil itself. During
this time, all the work devolved upon the squaws,
who, in tending the horses, and in packing wood
and water from a long distance, had their time
sufficiently occupied.   As there was little or no
grass in the vicinity, the animals were supported
entirely on the bark of the cotton-wood ; and to
procure this, the women were daily engaged in
felling huge trees, or climbing them fearlessly,
chopping off the upper limbs—springing like squirrels from branch to branch, which, in their confined costume, appeared matter of considerable
difficulty.

The most laughter-provoking scenes, however,
were, when a number of squaws sallied out to the
grove, with their long-nosed, wolfish-looking dogs
harnessed to their *travées* or trabogans, on which
loads of cotton-wood were piled.   The dogs, knowing full well the duty required of them, refuse to
approach the coaxing squaws, and, at the same
time, are fearful of provoking their anger by
escaping and running off.   They, therefore, squat
on their haunches, with tongues hanging out of
their long mouths, the picture of indecision, removing a short distance as the irate squaw
approaches.   When once harnessed to the travée,
however, which is simply a couple of lodge-poles
lashed on either side of the dog, with a couple of

cross-bars near the ends to support the freight,
they follow quietly enough, urged by bevies of
children, who invariably accompany the women.
Once arrived at the scene of their labours, the
reluctance of the curs to draw near the piles of
cotton-wood is most comical. They will lie down
stubbornly at a little distance, whining their un-
easiness, or sometimes scamper off bodily, with
their long poles trailing after them, pursued by
the yelling and half frantic squaws.

When the travées are laden, the squaws, bent
double under loads of wood sufficient to break a
porter's back, and calling to the dogs, which are
urged on by the buffalo-fed urchins in rear, lead
the line of march. The curs, taking advantage of
the helpless state of their mistresses, turn a deaf
ear to their coaxings, lying down every few yards
to rest, growling and fighting with each other, in
which encounters every cur joins the *mêlée*, charging pell-mell into the yelping throng, upsetting
the squalling children, and making confusion worse
confounded. Then, armed with lodge-poles, the
squaws, throwing down their loads, rush to the
rescue, dealing stalwart blows on the pugnacious
curs, and finally restoring something like order to
the march.

" Tszoo—tszoo !" they cry, " wah, kashne, ceit-
cha—get on, you devilish beasts—tszoo—tszoo !"
and belabouring them without mercy, they start
them into a gallop, which, once commenced, is

generally continued till they reach their destination.

The Indian dogs are, however, invariably well treated by the squaws, since they assist materially the every-day labours of these patient over-worked creatures, in hauling firewood to the lodge, and, on the line of march, carrying many of the household goods and chattels, which otherwise the squaw herself would have to carry on her back. Every lodge possesses from half-a-dozen to a score—some for draught and others for eating—for dog meat forms part and parcel of an Indian feast. The former are stout, wiry animals, half wolf half sheep-dog, and are regularly trained to draught; the latter are of a smaller kind, more inclined to fat, and embrace every variety of the genus cur. Many of the southern tribes possess a breed of dogs entirely divested of hair, which evidently have come from South America, and are highly esteemed for the kettle. Their meat, in appearance and flavour, resembles young pork, but far surpasses it in richness and delicacy.

The Sioux are very expert in making their lodges comfortable, taking more pains in their construction than most Indians. They are all of conical form : a framework of straight slender poles, resembling hop-poles, and from twenty to twenty-five feet long, is first erected, round which is stretched a sheeting of buffalo robes, softly dressed, and smoked to render them water-tight. The apex, through which

the ends of the poles protrude, is left open to allow
the smoke to escape. A small opening, sufficient to
permit the entrance of a man, is made on one side,
over which is hung a door of buffalo hide. A lodge
of the common size contains about twelve or fourteen skins, and contains comfortably a family of
twelve in number. The fire is made in the centre
immediately under the aperture in the roof, and a
flap of the upper skins is closed or extended at pleasure, serving as a cowl or chimney-top to regulate
the draught and permit the smoke to escape freely.
Round the fire, with their feet towards it, the
inmates sleep on skins and buffalo rugs, which are
rolled up during the day, and stowed at the back
of the lodge.

In travelling, the lodge-poles are secured half on
each side a horse, and the skins placed on transver-
sal bars near the ends, which trail along the ground,
—two or three squaws or children mounted on the
same horse, or the smallest of the latter borne in
the dog travées. A set of lodge-poles will last from
three to seven years, unless the village is constantly
on the move, when they are soon worn out in trailing over the gravelly prairie. They are usually of
ash, which grows on many of the mountain creeks,
and regular expeditions are undertaken when a
supply is required, either for their own lodges, or
for trading with those tribes who inhabit the prairies
at a great distance from the locality where the poles
are procured.

There are also certain creeks where the Indians resort to lay in a store of kinnik-kinnik (the inner bark
of the red willow), which they use as a substitute for
tobacco, and which has an aromatic and very pun-
gent flavour. It is prepared for smoking by being
scraped in thin curly flakes from the slender sap-
lings, and crisped before the fire, after which it is
rubbed between the hands into a form resembling
leaf-tobacco, and stored in skin bags for use. It has
a highly narcotic effect on those not habituated to its
use, and produces a heaviness sometimes approaching stupefaction, altogether different from the sooth-
ing effects of tobacco.

Every year, owing to the disappearance of the
buffalo from their former haunts, the Indians are
compelled to encroach upon each other's hunting-
grounds, which is a fruitful cause of war between
the different tribes. It is a curious fact, that the
buffalo retire before the whites, whilst the presence
of Indians in their pastures appears in no degree to
disturb them. Wherever a few white hunters are
congregated in a trading port, or elsewhere, so sure
it is that, if they remain in the same locality, the
buffalo will desert the vicinity, and seek pasture
elsewhere. In this, the Indians affirm, the wah-
keitcha, or " bad medicine," of the pale-faces is very
apparent; and they ground upon it their well-
founded complaints of the encroachments made upon
their hunting-grounds by the white hunters.

In the winter, many of the tribes are reduced to

K

the very verge of starvation—the buffalo having passed from their country into that of their enemies, when no other alternative is offered them, but to remain where they are and starve, or to follow the game into a hostile region, a move entailing war and all its horrors.

Reckless, moreover, of the future, in order to prepare robes for the traders, and to procure the pernicious fire-water, they wantonly slaughter, every year, vast numbers of buffalo cows (the skins of which sex only are dressed), and thus add to the evils in store for them. When questioned on this subject, and reproached with such want of foresight, they answer, that however quickly the buffalo disappears, the Red man "goes under" more quickly still; and that the Great Spirit has ordained that both shall be "rubbed out" from the face of nature at one and the same time,—"that arrows and bullets are not more fatal to the buffalo than the small-pox and fire-water to them, and that before many winters' snows have disappeared, the buffalo and the Red man will only be remembered by their bones, which will strew the plains."— "They look forward, however, to a future state, when, after a long journey, they will reach the happy hunting-grounds, where buffalo will once more blacken the prairies; where the pale-faces dare not come to disturb them; where no winter snows cover the ground, and the buffalo are always plentiful and fat."

As soon as the streams opened, La Bonté, now reduced to two animals and four traps, sallied forth again, this time seeking the dangerous country of the Blackfeet, on the head waters of the Yellow Stone and Upper Missouri. He was accompanied by three others, a man named Wheeler, and one Cross-Eagle, a Swede, who had been many years in the western country. Reaching the forks of a small creek, on both of which appeared plenty of beaver sign, La Bonté followed the left-hand one alone, whilst the others trapped the right in company, the former leaving his squaw in the company of a Sioux woman, who followed the fortunes of Cross-Eagle, the party agreeing to rendezvous at the junction of the two forks as soon as they had trapped to their heads and again descended them. The larger party were the first to reach the rendezvous, and camped on the banks of the main stream to await the arrival of La Bonté.

The morning after their return, they had just risen from their blankets, and were lazily stretching themselves before the fire, when a volley of fire-arms rattled from the bank of the creek, and two of their number fell dead to the ground, whilst at the same moment the deafening yells of Indians broke upon the ears of the frightened squaws. Cross-Eagle seized his rifle, and, though severely wounded, rushed to the cover of a hollow tree which stood near, and crawling into it, defended himself the whole day with the greatest obstinacy, killing

five Indians outright, and wounding several more.
Unable to drive the gallant trapper from his retreat,
the savages took advantage of a favourable wind
which suddenly sprang up, and fired the long dry
grass surrounding the tree. The rotten log catching fire, at length compelled the hunter to leave his
retreat. Clubbing his rifle, he charged amongst the
Indians, and fell at last, pierced through and through
with wounds, but not until two more of his assailants had fallen by his hand.

The two squaws were carried off, and one was
sold shortly afterwards to some white men at the
trading ports on the Platte; but La Bonté never
recovered the " Bending Reed," nor even heard of
her existence from that day. So once more was
the mountaineer bereft of his better half; and when
he returned to the rendezvous, a troop of wolves
were feasting on the bodies of his late companions,
and of the Indians killed in the affray, of which he
only heard the particulars a long time after from a
trapper, who had been present when one of the
squaws was offered at the trading post for sale, and
had heard her recount the miserable fate of her
husband and his companions on the forks of the
creek, which, from the fact of La Bonté being the
leader of the party, has since borne his name.

Undaunted by this misfortune, the trapper continued his solitary hunt, passing through the midst
of the Crow and Blackfeet country; encountering
many perils, often hunted by the Indians, but always

escaping. He had soon loaded both his animals with
beaver, and then thought of bending his steps to
some of the trading rendezvous on the other side of
the mountains, where employés of the Great North-
west Fur Company meet the trappers with the produce of their hunts, on Lewis's fork of the Columbia,
or one of its numerous affluents. His intention was
to pass the winter at some of the company's trading
posts in Oregon, into which country he had never
yet penetrated.

CHAPTER V.

WE have said that La Bonté was a philosopher:
he took the streaks of ill luck which checkered
his mountain life with perfect carelessness, if
not with stoical indifference. Nothing ruffled his
danger-steeled equanimity of temper; no sudden
emotion disturbed his mind. We have seen how
wives were torn from him without eliciting a groan
or grumble, (but such *contretemps*, it may be said,
can scarcely find a place in the category of ills);
how the loss of mules and mustangs, harried by
horse-stealing Indians, left him in the *ne-plus-ultra*
of mountain misery—" afoot; " how packs and
peltries, the hard-earned " beaver " of his perilous
hunts, were " raised " at one fell swoop by free-
booting bands of savages. Hunger and thirst, we
know, were commonplace sensations to the mountaineer. His storm-hardened flesh scarce felt the
pinging wounds of arrow-point or bullet; and when
in the midst of Indian fight, it is not probable that
any tender qualms of feeling would allay the itching of his fingers for his enemy's scalp-lock, nor
would any remains of civilised fastidiousness pre-

vent his burying his knife again and again in the
life-blood of an Indian savage.

Still, in one dark corner of his heart, there shone
at intervals a faint spark of what was once a fierce-
ly-burning fire. Neither time, that corroder of
all things, nor change, that ready abettor of oblivion, nor scenes of peril and excitement, which act
as dampers to more quiet memories, could smother
this little smouldering spark, which now and again
—when rarely-coming calm succeeded some stirring
passage in the hunter's life, and left him, for a brief
time, devoid of care, and victim to his thoughts—
would flicker suddenly, and light up all the nooks
and corners of his rugged breast, and discover to
his mind's eye that one deep-rooted memory clung
there still, though long neglected; proving that,
spite of time and change, of life and fortune,

" On revient tojours à ses premiers amours."

Often and often as La Bonté sat cross-legged
before his solitary camp-fire, and, pipe in mouth,
watched the blue smoke curling upwards in the
clear cold sky, a well-remembered form appeared
to gaze upon him from the vapoury wreaths. Then
would old recollections crowd before him, and old
emotions, long a stranger to his breast, shape themselves, as it were, into long-forgotten but now familiar pulsations. Again he felt the soft subduing
influence which once, in days gone by, a certain
passion exercised over his mind and body ; and
often a trembling seized him, the same he used to

experience at the sudden sight of one Mary Brand, whose dim and dreamy apparition so often watched his lonely bed, or, unconsciously conjured up, cheered him in the dreary watches of the long and stormy winter nights.

At first he only knew that one face haunted his dreams by night, and the few moments by day when he thought of any thing, and this face smiled lovingly upon him, and cheered him mightily. Name he had quite forgotten, or recalled it vaguely, and, setting small store by it, had thought of it no more.

For many years after he had deserted his home, La Bonté had cherished the idea of again returning to his country. During this period he had never forgotten his old flame, and many a choice fur he had carefully laid by, intended as a present for Mary Brand; and many a *gâge d'amour* of cunning shape and device, worked in stained quills of porcupine and bright-coloured beads—the handiwork of nimble-fingered squaws—he had packed in his possible sack for the same destination, hoping a time would come when he might lay them at her feet.

Year after year wore on, however, and still found him, with traps and rifle, following his perilous avocation; and each succeeding one saw him more and more wedded to the wild mountain-life. He was conscious how unfitted he had become again to enter the galling harness of conventionality and civilisation. He thought, too, how changed in manners and appearance he now must be, and could not believe that he would again find favour in the eyes of his quondam love, who, he judged, had long since forgotten him ; and inexperienced as he was in such matters, yet he knew enough of womankind to feel assured that time and absence had long since done the work, if even the natural fickleness of woman's nature had lain dormant. Thus it was that he came to forget Mary Brand, but still remembered the all-absorbing feeling she had once created in his breast, the shadow of which still remained, and often took form and feature in the smoke-wreaths of his solitary camp-fire.

If truth be told, La Bonté had his failings as a mountaineer, and—sin unpardonable in hunter law —still possessed, in holes and corners of his breast seldom explored by his inward eye, much of the leaven of kindly human nature, which now and again involuntarily peeped out, as greatly to the contempt of his comrade trappers as it was blushingly repressed by the mountaineer himself. Thus, in his various matrimonial episodes, he treated his dusky *sposas* with all the consideration the sex could possibly demand from hand of man. No squaw of his ever humped shoulder to receive a castigatory and marital " lodge-poling " for offence domestic ; but often has his helpmate blushed to see her pale-face lord and master devote himself to the feminine labour of packing huge piles of fire-wood

on his back, felling trees, butchering unwieldy buffalo—all which are included in the Indian category
of female duties.   Thus he was esteemed an excellent *parti* by all the marriageable young squaws of
Blackfoot, Crow, and Shoshone, of Yutah, Shian,
and Arapaho; but after his last connubial catas-
trophe, he steeled his heart against all the charms
and coquetry of Indian belles, and persevered in
unblessed widowhood for many a long day.

From the point where we left him on his way to
the waters of the Columbia, we must jump with
him over a space of nearly two years, during which
time he had a most uninterrupted run of good luck;
trapping with great success on the head streams of
the Columbia and Yellow Stone—the most dangerous of trapping ground—and finding good market
for his peltries at the " North-west" posts—beaver
fetching as high a price as five and six dollars a
" plew"—the " golden age" of trappers, now, alas,
never to return, and existing only in the fond
memory of the mountaineers.   This glorious time,
however, was too good to last.   In mountain language, " such heap of fat meat was not going to
' shine' much longer."

La Bonté was at this time one of a band of eight
trappers, whose hunting ground was about the
head waters of the Yellow Stone, which we have
before said is in the country of the Blackfeet.
With him were Killbuck, Meek, Marcellin, and
three others; and the leader of the party was Bill

Williams, that old " hard case " who had spent
forty years and more in the mountains, until he
had become as tough as the parflêche soles of his
moccasins.   They were all good men and true,
expert hunters, and well-trained mountaineers.
After having trapped all the streams they were
acquainted with, it was determined to strike into
the mountains, at a point where old Williams
affirmed, from the " run " of the hills, there must
be plenty of water, although not one of the party
had before explored the country, or knew any
thing of its nature, or of the likelihood of its affording game for themselves or pasture for their animals.   However, they packed their peltry, and put
out for the land in view—a lofty peak, dimly seen
above the more regular summit of the chain, being
their landmark.

For the first day or two their route lay between
two ridges of mountains, and by following the little
valley which skirted a creek, they kept on level
ground, and saved their animals considerable labour
and fatigue.   Williams always rode ahead, his body
bent over his saddle-horn, across which rested a
long heavy rifle, his keen gray eyes peering from
under the slouched brim of a flexible felt-hat, black
and shining with grease.   His buckskin hunting-
shirt, bedaubed until it had the appearance of
polished leather, hung in folds over his bony
carcass ; his nether extremities being clothed in
pantaloons of the same material (with scattered
fringes down the outside of the leg—which orna-

ments, however, had been pretty well thinned to
supply " whangs " for mending moccasins or pack-
saddles), which, shrunk with wet, clung tightly to
his long, spare, sinewy legs. His feet were thrust
into a pair of Mexican stirrups made of wood, and
as big as coal-scuttles; and iron spurs of incredible
proportions, with tinkling drops attached to the
rowels, were fastened to his heel—a bead-worked
strap, four inches broad, securing them over the in-
step. In the shoulder-belt which sustained his
powder-horn and bullet-pouch, were fastened the
various instruments essential to one pursuing his
mode of life. An awl, with deer-horn handle, and
the point defended by a case of cherry-wood carved
by his own hand, hung at the back of the belt, side
by side with a worm for cleaning the rifle; and
under this was a squat and quaint-looking bullet-
mould, the handles guarded by strips of buckskin
to save his fingers from burning when running balls,
having for its companion a little bottle made from
the point of an antelope's horn, scraped transparent,
which contained the " medicine " used in baiting the
traps. The old coon's face was sharp and thin, a
long nose and chin hob-nobbing each other; and his
head was always bent forward giving him the appearance of being hump-backed. He *appeared* to
look neither to the right nor left, but, in fact, his
little twinkling eye was everywhere. He looked at
no one he was addressing, always seeming to be
thinking of something else than the subject of his

discourse, speaking in a whining, thin, cracked voice,
and in a tone that left the hearer in doubt whether
he was laughing or crying. On the present occasion he had joined this band, and naturally assumed
the leadership (for Bill ever refused to go in harness), in opposition to his usual practice, which was
to hunt alone. His character was well known. Acquainted with every inch of the Far West, and with
all the Indian tribes who inhabited it, he never failed
to outwit his Red enemies, and generally made his
appearance at the rendezvous, from his solitary expeditions, with galore of beaver, when numerous
bands of trappers dropped in on foot, having been
despoiled of their packs and animals by the very
Indians through the midst of whom old Williams
had contrived to pass unseen and unmolested. On
occasions when he had been in company with others,
and attacked by Indians, Bill invariably fought manfully, and with all the coolness that perfect indifference to death or danger could give, but always " on
his own hook." His rifle cracked away merrily,
and never spoke in vain ; and in a charge—if ever
it came to that—his keen-edged butcher-knife tickled
the fleece of many a Blackfoot. But at the same
time, if he saw that discretion was the better part of
valour, and affairs wore so cloudy an aspect as to
render retreat advisable, he would first express his
opinion in curt terms, and decisively, and, charging
up his rifle, would take himself off and "cache"* so

* Hide—from *cacher*.

effectually that to search for him was utterly useless.
Thus, when with a large party of trappers, when
any thing occurred which gave him a hint that
trouble was coming, or more Indians were about
than he considered good for his animals, Bill was
wont to exclaim—

"Do 'ee hyar now, boys, thar's sign about? this
hos feels like caching;" and, without more words,
and stoically deaf to all remonstrances, he would
forthwith proceed to pack his animals, talking the
while to an old, crop-eared, raw-boned Nez-percé
pony, his own particular saddle-horse, who in dogged temper and iron hardiness, was a worthy companion of his self-willed master. This beast, as Bill
seized his apishamore to lay upon its galled back,
would express displeasure by humping its back and
shaking its withers with a wincing motion, that
always excited the ire of the old trapper; and no
sooner had he laid the apishamore smoothly on the
chafed skin, than a wriggle of the animal shook it
off.

"Do 'ee hyar now, you darned crittur?" he would
whine out, "can't 'ee keep quiet your old fleece now?
Isn't this old coon putting out to save 'ee from the
darned Injuns now, do 'ee hyar?" And then, continuing his work and taking no notice of his comrades,
who stood by bantering the eccentric old trapper,
he would soliloquise—"Do 'ee hyar, now? This
niggur sees sign ahead—he does; he'll be afoot
afore long, if he don't keep his eye skinned,—*he*

will. *Injuns* is all about, they ar': Blackfoot at that. Can't come round this child—they can't, wagh!" And at last, his pack animals securely tied to the tail of his horse, he would mount, and throwing the rifle across the horn of his saddle, and without noticing his companions, would drive the jingling spurs into his horse's gaunt sides, and muttering, " Can't come round this child—they can't !" would ride away ; and nothing more would be seen or heard of him perhaps for months, when they would not unfrequently, themselves bereft of animals in the scrape he had foreseen, find him located in some solitary valley, in his lonely camp, with his animals securely picketed around, and his peltries safe.

However, if he took it into his head to keep company with a party, all felt perfectly secure under his charge. His iron frame defied fatigue, and, at night, his love for himself and his own animals was sufficient guarantee that the camp would be well guarded. As he rode ahead, his spurs jingling, and thumping the sides of his old horse at every step, he managed, with admirable dexterity, to take advantage of the best line of country to follow— avoiding the gullies and cañons and broken ground, which would otherwise have impeded his advance. This tact appeared instinctive, for he looked neither right nor left, whilst continuing a course as straight as possible at the foot of the mountains. In selecting a camping site, he displayed equal skill : wood, water, and grass began to fill his thoughts towards sundown, and when these three requisites for a camping ground presented themselves, old Bill sprang from his saddle, unpacked his animals in a twinkling, and hobbled them, struck fire and ignited a few chips (leaving the rest to pack in the wood), lit his pipe, and enjoyed himself. On one occasion, when passing through the valley, they had come upon a band of fine buffalo cows, and, shortly after camping, two of the party rode in with a good supply of fat fleece. One of the party was a "greenhorn" on his first hunt, fresh from a fort on Platte, and as yet uninitiated in the mysteries of mountain cooking. Bill, lazily smoking his pipe, called to him, as he happened to be nearest, to butcher off a piece of meat and put it in his pot. Markhead seized the fleece, and commenced innocently carving off a huge ration, when a gasping roar from the old trapper caused him to drop his knife.

"Ti-ya," growled Bill, "do 'ee hyar, now, you darned greenhorn, do 'ee spile fat cow like that whar you was raised? Them doins wont shine in this crowd, boy, do 'ee hyar, darned you? What! butcher meat across the grain! why, whar'll the blood be goin' to, you precious Spaniard? Down the grain, I say," he continued in a severe tone of rebuke, "and let your flaps be long, or out the juice 'll run slick—do 'ee hyar, now?" But this heretical error nearly cost the old trapper his appetite, and all night long he grumbled his horror at seeing "fat cow spiled in that fashion."

When two or three days' journey brought them
to the end of the valley, and they commenced the
passage of the mountain, their march was obstructed
by all kinds of obstacles; although they had chosen
what appeared to be a gap in the chain, and what
was in fact the only practicable passage in that vicinity.   They followed the cañon of a branch of the
Yellow Stone, where it entered the mountain; but
from this point it became a torrent, and it was only
by dint of incredible exertions that they reached
the summit of the ridge.   Game was exceedingly
scarce in the vicinity, and they suffered extremely
from hunger, having, on more than one occasion,
recourse to the parflêche soles of their moccasins to
allay its pangs. Old Bill, however, never grumbled;
he chewed away at his shoes with relish even, and as
long as he had a pipeful of tobacco in his pouch,
was a happy man.   Starvation was as yet far off,
for all their animals were in existence; but as they
were in a country where it was difficult to procure
a remount, each trapper hesitated to sacrifice one of
his horses to his appetite.

From the summit of the ridge, Bill recognised the
country on the opposite side to that whence they
had just ascended as familiar to him, and pronounced
it to be full of beaver, as well as abounding in the
less desirable commodity of Indians.   This was the
valley lying about the lakes now called Eustis and
Biddle, in which are many thermal and mineral
springs, well known to the trappers by the names

L

of the Soda, Beer, and Brimstone Springs, and regarded by them with no little awe and curiosity, as being the breathing-places of his Satanic majesty —considered, moreover, to be the "biggest kind" of "medicine" to be found in the mountains.   If truth be told, old Bill hardly relished the idea of entering this country, which he pronounced to be of "bad medicine" notoriety, but nevertheless agreed to guide them to the best trapping ground.

One day they reached a creek full of beaver sign, and determined to halt here and establish their headquarters, while they trapped in the neighbour-hood.   We must here observe, that at this period— which was one of considerable rivalry amongst the various trading companies in the Indian territory— the Indians, having become possessed of arms and ammunition in great quantities, had grown unu-sually daring and persevering in their attacks on the white hunters who passed through their coun-try, and consequently the trappers were compelled to roam about in larger bands for mutual protection, which, although it made them less liable to open attack, yet rendered it more difficult for them to pursue their calling without being discovered; for, where one or two men might pass unseen, the broad trail of a large party, with its animals, was not likely to escape the sharp eyes of the cunning savages.

They had scarcely encamped when the old leader, who had sallied out a short distance from camp to reconnoitre the neighbourhood, returned with an Indian moccasin in his hand, and informed his companions that its late owner and others were about.

" Do 'ee hyar now, boys, thar's *Injuns* knocking round, and Blackfoot at that; but thar's plenty of beaver too, and this child means trapping any how."

His companions were anxious to leave such dangerous vicinity; but the old fellow, contrary to his usual caution, determined to remain where he was —saying that there were Indians all over the country for that matter; and as they had determined to hunt here, he had made up his mind too—which was conclusive, and all agreed to stop where they were, in spite of the Indians. La Bonté killed a couple of mountain sheep close to camp, and they feasted rarely on the fat mutton that night, and were unmolested by marauding Blackfeet.

The next morning, leaving two of their number in camp, they started in parties of two, to hunt for beaver sign and set their traps. Markhead paired with one Batiste, Killbuck and La Bonté formed another couple, Meek and Marcellin another; two Canadians trapped together, and Bill Williams and another remained to guard the camp: but this last, leaving Bill mending his moccasins, started off to kill a mountain sheep, a band of which animals was visible.

Markhead and his companion, the first couple on the list, followed a creek, which entered that on which they had encamped, about ten miles distant. Beaver sign was abundant, and they had set eight traps, when Markhead came suddenly upon fresh Indian sign, where squaws had passed through the shrubbery on the banks of the stream to procure water, as he knew from observing a large stone placed by them in the stream, on which to stand to enable them to dip their kettles in the deepest water. Beckoning to his companion to follow, and cocking his rifle, he carefully pushed aside the bushes, and noiselessly proceeded up the bank, when, creeping on hands and knees, he gained the top, and, looking from his hiding-place, descried three Indian huts standing on a little plateau near the creek. Smoke curled from the roofs of branches, but the skin doors were carefully closed, so that he was unable to distinguish the number of the inmates. At a little distance, however, he observed two or three squaws gathering wood, with the usual attendance of curs, whose acuteness in detecting the scent of strangers was much to be dreaded.

Markhead was a rash and daring young fellow, caring no more for Indians than he did for prairie dogs, and acting ever on the spur of the moment, and as his inclination dictated, regardless of consequences. He at once determined to enter the lodges, and attack the enemy, should any be there; and the other trapper was fain to join him in the enterprise. The lodges proved empty, but the fires were still burning, and meat cooking upon them, to which

the hungry hunters did ample justice, besides helping themselves to whatever goods and chattels,
in the shape of leather and moccasins, took their
fancy.

Gathering their spoil into a bundle, they sought
their horses, which they had left tied under cover
of the timber on the banks of the creek; and,
mounting, took the back trail, to pick up their traps
and remove from so dangerous a neighbourhood.
They were approaching the spot where the first
trap was set, a thick growth of ash and quaking-ash
concealing the stream, when Markhead, who was
riding ahead, observed the bushes agitated, as if
some animal was making its way through them.
He instantly stopped his horse, and his companion
rode to his side, to inquire the cause of this abrupt
halt. They were within a few yards of the belt of
shrubs which skirted the stream; and before Markhead had time to reply, a dozen swarthy heads and
shoulders suddenly protruded from the leafy
screen, and as many rifle-barrels and arrows were
pointing at their breasts. Before the trappers
had time to turn their horses and fly, a cloud
of smoke burst from the thicket almost in their
faces. Batiste, pierced with several balls, fell dead,
and Markhead felt himself severely wounded. However, he struck the spurs into his horse; and as
some half-score Blackfeet jumped with loud cries
from their cover, he discharged his rifle amongst
them, and galloped off, a volley of balls and arrows

whistling after him. He drew no bit until he reined
up at the camp-fire, where he found Bill quietly
dressing a deer-skin. That worthy looked up from
his work; and seeing Markhead's face streaming
with blood, and the very unequivocal evidence of an
Indian rencontre in the shape of an arrow sticking
in his back, he asked,—" Do 'ee feel bad now, boy?
Whar away you see them darned Blackfoot?"

" Well, pull this arrow out of my back, and may
be I'll feel like telling," answered Markhead.

" Do 'ee hyar now! hold on till I've grained this
cussed skin, will 'ee! Did 'ee ever see sich a darned
pelt, now? it won't take the smoke any how I fix
it." And Markhead was fain to wait the leisure of
the imperturbable old trapper, before he was eased
of his annoying companion.

Old Bill expressed no surprise or grief when
informed of the fate of poor Batiste. He said it
was " just like greenhorns, runnin' into them cussed
Blackfoot;" and observed that the defunct trapper,
being only a Vide-pôche, was " no account anyhow."
Presently Killbuck and La Bonté galloped into
camp, with another alarm of Indians. They had
also been attacked suddenly by a band of Blackfeet,
but, being in a more open country, had got clear
off, after killing two of their assailants, whose scalps
hung at the horns of their saddles. They had been
in a different direction to that in which Markhead and
his companion had proceeded, and, from the signs
they had observed, expressed their belief that the

country was alive with Indians. Neither of these
men had been wounded. Presently the two Canadians made their appearance on the bluff, galloping
with might and main to camp, and shouting " Indians, Indians," as they came. All being assembled,
and a council held, it was determined to abandon
the camp and neighbourhood immediately. Old Bill
was already packing his animals, and as he pounded
the saddle down on the withers of his old Rosinante,
he muttered,—" Do 'ee hyar, now! this coon 'ull
câche, *he* will." So mounting his horse, and leading his pack mule by a lariat, he bent over his
saddle-horn, dug his ponderous rowels into the lank
sides of his beast, and, without a word, struck up
the bluff and disappeared.

The others, hastily gathering up their packs, and
most of them having lost their traps, quickly followed his example, and " put out." On cresting
the high ground which rose from the creek, they
observed thin columns of smoke mounting into the
air from many different points, the meaning of
which they were at no loss to guess. However
they were careful not to show themselves on elevated ground, keeping as much as possible under
the banks of the creek, when such a course was
practicable; but, the bluffs sometimes rising precipitously from the water, they were more than once
compelled to ascend the banks, and continue their
course along the uplands, whence they might easily
be discovered by the Indians. It was nearly sun-

down when they left their camp, but they proceeded during the greater part of the night at as rapid a rate as possible; their progress, however, being greatly retarded as they advanced into the mountain, their route lying up stream. Towards morning they halted for a brief space, but started again as soon as daylight permitted them to see their way over the broken ground.

The creek now forced its way through a narrow cañon, the banks being thickly clothed with a shrubbery of cottonwood and quaking-ash. The mountain rose on each side, but not abruptly, being here and there broken into plateaus and shelving prairies. In a very thick bottom, sprinkled with coarse grass, they halted about noon, and removed the saddles and packs from their wearied animals, picketing them in the best spots of grass.

La Bonté and Killbuck, after securing their animals, left the camp to hunt, for they had no provisions of any kind; and a short distance beyond it, the former came suddenly upon a recent moccasin track in the timber. After examining it for a moment, he raised his head with a broad grin, and, turning to his companion, pointed into the cover, where, in the thickest part, they discerned the well-known figure of old Bill's horse, browsing upon the cherry bushes. Pushing through the thicket in search of the brute's master, La Bonté suddenly stopped short as the muzzle of a rifle-barrel gaped before his eyes at the distance of a few inches, whilst the thin voice of Bill muttered—

" Do 'ee hyar now, I was nigh giving 'ee h——: I *was* now. If I didn't think 'ee was Blackfoot, I'm dogged now." And not a little indignant was the old fellow that his câche had been so easily, though accidentally, discovered. However, he presently made his appearance in camp, leading his animals, and once more joined his late companions, not deigning to give any explanation as to why or wherefore he had deserted them the day before, merely muttering, " do 'ee hyar now, thar's trouble comin.' "

The two hunters returned after sundown with a black-tailed deer; and after eating the better part of the meat, and setting a guard, the party were glad to roll in their blankets and enjoy the rest they so much needed. They were undisturbed during the night; but at dawn of day the sleepers were roused by a hundred fierce yells, from the mountains enclosing the creek on which they had encamped. The yells were instantly followed by a ringing volley, the bullets thudding into the trees, and cutting the branches near them, but without causing any mischief. Old Bill rose from his blanket and shook himself, and exclaimed "Wagh!" as at that moment a ball plumped into the fire over which he was standing, and knocked the ashes about in a cloud. All the mountaineers seized their

rifles and sprang to cover; but as yet it was not
sufficiently light to show them their enemy, the
bright flashes from the guns alone indicating their
position. As morning dawned, however, they saw
that both sides of the cañon were occupied by the
Indians; and, from the firing, judged there must
be at least a hundred warriors engaged in the
attack. Not a shot had yet been fired by the
trappers, but as the light increased, they eagerly
watched for an Indian to expose himself, and offer
a mark to their trusty rifles. La Bonté, Killbuck,
and old Bill, lay a few yards distant from each
other, flat on their faces, near the edge of the
thicket, their rifles raised before them, and the
barrels resting in the forks of convenient bushes.
From their place of concealment to the position of
the Indians—who, however, were scattered here and
there, wherever a rock afforded them cover—was a
distance of about a hundred and fifty yards, or
within fair rifle-shot. The trappers were obliged
to divide their force, since both sides of the creek
were occupied; but, such was the nature of the
ground, and the excellent cover afforded by the
rocks and boulders, and clumps of dwarf pine and
hemlock, that not a hand's-breadth of an Indian's
body had yet been seen. Nearly opposite La Bonté,
a shelving glade in the mountain side ended in an
abrupt precipice, and at the very edge, and almost
toppling over it, were several boulders, just of sufficient size to afford cover to a man's body. As

this bluff overlooked the trappers' position, it was
occupied by the Indians, and every rock covered
an assailant. At one point, just over where La
Bonté and Killbuck were lying, two boulders lay
together, with just sufficient interval to admit a
rifle-barrel between them, and from this breastwork
an Indian kept up a most annoying fire. All his
shots fell in dangerous propinquity to one or other
of the trappers, and already Killbuck had been
grazed by one better directed than the others. La
Bonté watched for some time in vain for a chance
to answer this persevering marksman, and at length
an opportunity offered, by which he was not long
in profiting.

The Indian, as the light increased, was better
able to discern his mark, and fired, and yelled every
time he did so, with redoubled vigour. In his
eagerness, and probably whilst in the act of taking
aim, he leaned too heavily against the rock which
covered him, and, detaching it from its position,
down it rolled into the cañon, exposing his body by
its fall. At the same instant, a wreath of smoke
puffed from the bushes which concealed the trappers,
and the crack of La Bonté's rifle spoke the first
word of reply to the Indian challenge. A few
feet behind the rock, fell the dead body of the
Indian, rolling down the steep sides of the cañon,
and only stopped by a bush at the very bottom,
within a few yards of the spot where Markhead lay
concealed in some high grass.

That daring fellow instantly jumped from his cover, and drawing his knife, rushed to the body, and in another moment held aloft the Indian's scalp, giving, at the same time, a triumphant whoop. A score of rifles were levelled and discharged at the intrepid mountaineer; but in the act many Indians incautiously exposed themselves, every rifle in the timber cracked simultaneously, and for each report an Indian bit the dust.

Now, however, they changed their tactics. Finding they were unable to drive the trappers from their position, they retired from the mountain, and the firing suddenly ceased. In their retreat they were forced to expose themselves, and again the whites dealt destruction amongst them. As the Indians retired, yelling loudly, the hunters thought they had given up the contest; but presently a cloud of smoke rising from the bottom immediately below them, at once discovered the nature of their plans. A brisk wind was blowing up the cañon; and, favoured by it, they fired the brush on the banks of the stream, knowing that before this the hunters must speedily retreat.

Against such a result, but for the gale of wind which drove the fire roaring before it, they could have provided—for your mountaineer never fails to find resources on a pinch. They would have fired the brush to leeward of their position, and also carefully ignited that to windward, or between them and the advancing flame, extinguishing it

immediately when a sufficient space had thus
been cleared, over which the flame could not
leap, and thus cutting themselves off from it both
above and below their position. In the present
instance they could not profit by such a course, as
the wind was so strong that, if once the bottom
caught fire, they would not be able to extinguish
it; besides which, in the attempt, they would so
expose themselves that they would be picked off by
the Indians without difficulty. As it was, the fire
came roaring before the wind with the speed of a
race-horse, and, spreading from the bottom, licked
the mountain sides, the dry grass burning like tinder. Huge volumes of stifling smoke rolled before
it, and, in a very few minutes, the trappers were
hastily mounting their animals, driving the packed
ones before them. The dense clouds of smoke concealed every thing from their view, and, to avoid this,
they broke from the creek and galloped up the sides
of the cañon on to the more level plateau. As they
attained this, a band of mounted Indians charged
them. One, waving a red blanket, dashed through
the cavallada, and was instantly followed by all the
loose animals of the trappers, the rest of the Indians
pursuing with loud shouts. So sudden was the
charge, that the whites had not power to prevent
the stampede. Old Bill, as usual, led his pack
mules by the lariat; but the animals, mad with
terror at the shouts of the Indians, broke from him,
nearly pulling him out of his seat at the same time.

To cover the retreat of the others with their prey, a band of mounted Indians now appeared, threatening an attack in front, whilst their first assailants, rushing from the bottom, at least a hundred strong, assaulted in rear. "Do 'ee hyar, boys!" shouted old Bill, "break, or you'll go under. This child's goin' to câche!" and saying the word, off he went. *Sauve-qui-peut* was the order of the day, and not a moment too soon, for overwhelming numbers were charging upon them, and the mountain resounded with savage yells. La Bonté and Killbuck stuck together: they saw old Bill, bending over his saddle, dive right into the cloud of smoke, and apparently make for the creek bottom—their other companions scattering each on his own hook, and saw no more of them for many a month; and thus was one of the most daring and successful bands broken up that ever trapped in the mountains of the Far West.

It is painful to follow the steps of the poor fellows who, thus despoiled of the hardly-earned produce of their hunt, saw all their wealth torn from them at one swoop. The two Canadians were killed upon the night succeeding that of the attack. Worn with fatigue, hungry and cold, they had built a fire in what they thought was a secure retreat, and, rolled in their blankets, were soon buried in a sleep from which they never awoke. An Indian boy tracked them, and watched their camp. Burning with the idea of signalising himself thus early, he awaited his

opportunity, and noiselessly approaching their resting-place, shot them both with arrows, and returned
in triumph to his people with their horses and
scalps.

La Bonté and Killbuck sought a passage in the
mountain by which to cross over to the head waters
of the Columbia, and there fall in with some of the
traders or trappers of the North-west. They
became involved in the mountains, in a part where
was no game of any description, and no pasture for
their miserable animals. One of these they killed
for food; the other, a bag of bones, died from sheer
starvation. They had very little ammunition, their
moccasins were worn out, and they were unable to
procure skins to supply themselves with fresh ones.
Winter was fast approaching; the snow already
covered the mountains; and storms of sleet and hail
poured incessantly through the valleys, benumbing
their exhausted limbs, hardly protected by scanty
and ragged covering. To add to their miseries,
poor Killbuck was taken ill. He had been wounded
in the groin by a bullet some time before, and the
ball still remained. The wound, aggravated by
walking and the excessive cold, assumed an ugly
appearance, and soon rendered him incapable of
sustained exertion, all motion even being attended
with intolerable pain. La Bonté had made a shanty
for his suffering companion, and spread a soft bed
of pine branches for him, by the side of a small
creek at the point where it came out of the moun-

tain and followed its course through a little prairie. They had been three days without other food than a piece of parflêche, which had formed the back of La Bonté's bullet-pouch, and which, after soaking in the creek, they eagerly devoured. Killbuck was unable to move, and sinking fast from exhaustion. His companion had hunted from morning till night, as well as his failing strength would allow him, but had not seen the traces of any kind of game, with the exception of some old buffalo tracks, made apparently months before by a band of bulls crossing the mountain.

The morning of the fourth day La Bonté, as usual, rose at daybreak from his blanket, and was proceeding to collect wood for the fire during his absence while hunting, when Killbuck called to him, and in an almost inarticulate voice desired him to seat himself by his side.

"Boy," he said, "this old hos feels like goin' under, and that afore long. You're stout yet, and if thar was meat handy, you'd come round slick. Now, boy, I'll be under, as I said, afore many hours, and if you don't raise meat you'll be in the same fix. I never eat dead meat* myself, and wouldn't ask no one to do it neither; but meat fair killed is meat any way; so, boy, put your knife in this old niggur's lights, and help yourself. It's 'poor bull,' I know, but maybe it'll do to keep life in; and

* Carrion.

along the fleece thar's meat yet, and maybe my old hump ribs has picking on 'em."

"You're a good old hos," answered La Bonté, "but this child ain't turned niggur yet."

Killbuck then begged his companion to leave him to his fate, and strive himself to reach game; but this alternative La Bonté likewise generously refused, and faintly endeavouring to cheer the sick man, left him once again to look for game. He was so weak that he felt difficulty in supporting himself, and knowing how futile would be his attempts to hunt, he sallied from the camp convinced that a few hours more would see the last of him.

He had scarcely raised his eyes, when, hardly crediting his senses, he saw within a few hundred yards of him an old bull, worn with age, lying on the prairie. Two wolves were seated on their haunches before him, their tongues lolling from their mouths, whilst the buffalo was impotently rolling his ponderous head from side to side, his blood-shot eyes glaring fiercely at his tormentors, and flakes of foam, mixed with blood, dropping from his mouth over his long shaggy beard. La Bonté was transfixed; he scarcely dared to breathe, lest the animal should be alarmed and escape. Weak as it was, he could hardly have followed it, and, knowing that his own and companion's life hung upon the success of his shot, he scarcely had strength to raise his rifle. By dint of extraordinary exertions and precautions, which were totally unnecessary, for the poor old

M

bull had not a move in him, the hunter approached within shot. Lying upon the ground, he took a long steady aim, and fired. The buffalo raised its matted head, tossed it wildly for an instant, and, stretching out its limbs convulsively, turned over on its side and was dead.

Killbuck heard the shot, and crawling from under the little shanty which covered his bed, saw, to his astonishment, La Bonté in the act of butchering a buffalo within two hundred yards of camp. " Hurraw for you!" he faintly exclaimed; and exhausted by the exertion he had used, and perhaps by the excitement of an anticipated feast, fell back and fainted.

However, the killing was the easiest matter, for when the huge carcass lay dead upon the ground, our hunter had hardly strength to drive the blade of his knife through the tough hide of the old patriarch. Then having cut off as much of the meat as he could carry, eating the while sundry portions of the liver, which he dipped in the gall-bladder by way of relish, La Bonté cast a wistful look upon the half-starved wolves, who now loped round and round, licking their chops, only waiting until his back was turned to fall to with appetite equal to his own, and capabilities of swallowing and digesting far superior. La Bonté looked at the buffalo and then at the wolves, levelled his rifle and shot one dead, at which the survivor scampered off without delay.

Arrived at camp, packing in a tolerable load of

the best part of the animal—for hunger lent him
strength—he found poor Killbuck lying on his back,
deaf to time, and to all appearance gone under.
Having no salvolatile or vinaigrette at hand, La
Bonté flapped a lump of raw fleece into his patient's
face, and this instantly revived him.   Then taking
the sick man's shoulder, he raised him tenderly into
a sitting posture, and invited, in kindly accents,
" the old hos to feed," thrusting at the same time a
tolerable slice of liver into his hand, which the
patient looked at wistfully and vaguely for a few
short moments, and then greedily devoured.   It
was nightfall by the time that La Bonté, assisted by
many intervals of hard eating, packed in the last of
the meat, which formed a goodly pile around the
fire.

" Poor bull" it was in all conscience : the labour
of chewing a mouthful of the " tender loin" was
equal to a hard day's hunt; but to them, poor
starved fellows, it appeared the richest of meat.
They still preserved a small tin pot, and in this, by
stress of eternal boiling, La Bonté contrived to
make some strong soup, which soon restored his sick
companion to marching order.   For himself, as soon
as a good meal had filled him, he was strong as ever,
and employed himself in drying the remainder of
the meat for future use.   Even the wolf, bony as he
was, was converted into meat, and rationed them
several days.   Winter, however, had set in with
such severity, and Killbuck was still so weak, that

La Bonté determined to remain in his present position until spring, as he now found that buffalo frequently visited the valley, as it was more bare of snow than the lowlands, and afforded them better pasture; and one morning he had the satisfaction of seeing a band of seventeen bulls within long rifle-shot of the camp, out of which four of the fattest were soon laid low by his rifle.

They still had hard times before them, for towards spring the buffalo again disappeared; the greater part of their meat had been spoiled, owing to there not being sufficient sun to dry it thoroughly; and when they resumed their journey they had nothing to carry with them, and had a desert before them without game of any kind. We pass over what they suffered. Hunger and thirst were their portion, and Indians assaulted them at times, and many miraculous and hair-breadth escapes they had from these enemies.

CHAPTER VI.

THE trail to Oregon, followed by traders and emigrants, crosses the Rocky Mountains at a point
known as the South Pass, where a break in the
chain occurs of such moderate and gradual elevation, as to permit the passage of waggons with
tolerable facility. The Sweet Water Valley runs
nearly to the point where the dividing ridge of the
Pacific and Atlantic waters throws off its streams to
their respective oceans. At one end of this valley,
and situated on the right bank of the Sweet Water,
a huge isolated mass of granitic rock rises to the
height of three hundred feet, abruptly from the
plain. On the smooth and scarped surface presented by one of its sides, are rudely carved the
names and initials of traders, trappers, travellers,
and emigrants, who have here recorded the memo-
rial of their sojourn in the remote wilderness of the
Far West. The face of the rock is covered with
names familiar to the mountaineers as those of the
most renowned of their hardy brotherhood; while
others again occur, better known to the science and
literature of the Old World than to the unlearned
trappers of the Rocky Mountains. The huge mass

is a well-known landmark to the Indians and mountaineers; and travellers and emigrants hail it as the
half-way beacon between the frontiers of the United
States and the still distant goal of their long and
perilous journey.

It was a hot sultry day in July. Not a breath
of air relieved the intense and oppressive heat of
the atmosphere, unusual here, where pleasant summer breezes, and sometimes stronger gales, blow
over the elevated plains with the regularity of
trade-winds. The sun, at its meridian height, struck
the dry sandy plain and parched the drooping buf-
falo-grass on its surface, and its rays, refracted and
reverberating from the heated ground, distorted
every object seen through its lurid medium. Straggling antelope, leisurely crossing the adjoining
prairie, appeared to be gracefully moving in mid-
air; whilst a scattered band of buffalo bulls loomed
huge and indistinct in the vapoury distance. In
the timbered valley of the river, deer and elk were
standing motionless in the water, under the shade
of the overhanging cottonwoods, seeking a respite
from the persevering attacks of swarms of horse-
flies and musquitos; and now and then a heavy
splash was heard, as they tossed their antlered heads
into the stream, to free them from the venomous
insects that buzzed incessantly about them. In
the sandy prairie, beetles of an enormous size were
rolling in every direction huge balls of earth, pushing them with their hind legs with comical perse-

verance; cameleons darted about, assimilating the hue of their grotesque bodies with the colour of the sand: groups of prairie-dog houses were seen, each with its inmate barking lustily on the roof; whilst under cover of nearly every bush of sage or cactus a rattlesnake lay glittering in lazy coil. Tantalising the parched sight, the neighbouring peaks of the lofty Wind River Mountains glittered in a mantle of sparkling snow, whilst Sweet Water Mountain, capped in cloud, looked gray and cool, in striking contrast to the burned up plains which lay basking at its foot.

Resting their backs against the rock (on which, we have said, are *now* carved the names of many travellers), and defended from the powerful rays of the sun by its precipitous sides, two white men quietly slept. They were gaunt and lantern-jawed, and clothed in tattered buckskin. Each held a rifle across his knees, but—strange sight in this country —one had its pan thrown open, which was rust-eaten and contained no priming; the other's hammer was without a flint. Their faces were as if covered with mahogany-coloured parchment; their eyes were sunken; and as their jaws fell listlessly on their breasts, their cheeks were hollow, with the bones nearly protruding from the skin. One was in the prime of manhood, with handsome features; the other, considerably past middle age, was stark and stern. Months of dire privation had brought them to this pass. The elder of the two was Killbuck, of mountain fame ; the other was hight La Bonté.

The former opened his eyes, and saw the buffalo feeding on the plain. " Ho, boy," he said, touching his companion, " thar's meat a-runnin."

La Bonté looked in the direction the other pointed, stood up, and hitching round his pouch and powder-horn, drew the stopper from the latter with his teeth, and placing the mouth in the palm of his left hand, turned the horn up and shook it.

" Not a grain," he said—" not a grain, old hos."

" Wagh !" exclaimed the other, " we'll have to eat afore long," and rising, walked into the prairie. He had hardly stepped two paces, when, passing close to a sage bush, a rattlesnake whizzed a note of warning with its tail. Killbuck grinned, and taking the wiping-stick from his rifle-barrel, tapped the snake on the head, and, taking it by the tail, threw it to La Bonté, saying, " hyar's meat, any how." The old fellow followed up his success by slaying half-a-dozen more, and brought them in skewered through the head on his wiping-stick. A fire was soon kindled, and the snakes roasting before it ; when La Bonté, who sat looking at the buffalo which fed close to the rock, suddenly saw them raise their heads, snuff the air, and scamper towards him. A few minutes afterwards a huge shapeless body loomed in the refracted air, approaching the spot where the buffalo had been grazing

The hunters looked at it and then at each other, and ejaculated " Wagh!" Presently a long white mass showed more distinctly, followed by another, and before each was a string of animals.

" Waggons, by hos and beaver! Hurrah for Conostoga!" exclaimed the trappers in a breath, as they now observed two white-tilted waggons, drawn by several pairs of mules, approaching the very spot where they sat. Several mounted men were riding about the waggons, and two on horseback, in advance of all, were approaching the rock, when they observed the smoke curling from the hunters' fire. They halted at sight of this, and one of the two, drawing a long instrument from a case, which Killbuck voted a rifle, directed it towards them for a moment, and then, lowering it, again moved forward.

As they drew near, the two poor trappers, although half-dead with joy, still retained their seats with Indian gravity and immobility of feature, turning now and then the crackling snakes which lay on the embers of the fire. The two strangers approached. One, a man of some fifty years of age, of middle height and stoutly built, was clad in a white shooting-jacket, of cut unknown in mountain tailoring, and a pair of trousers of the well-known material called " shepherd's plaid ;" a broad-brimmed Panama shaded his face, which was ruddy with health and exercise; a belt round the waist supported a handsome bowie-knife, and a double-barrelled fowling-piece was *slung* across his shoulder.

His companion was likewise dressed in a light shooting-jacket, of many pockets and dandy cut, rode on an English saddle and in *boots*, and was armed with a superb double rifle, glossy from the case, and bearing few marks of use or service. He was a tall, fine-looking fellow of thirty, with light hair and complexion; a scrupulous beard and mustache; a wide-awake hat, with a short pipe stuck in the band, not very black with smoke; an elaborate powder-horn over his shoulder, with a Cairngorm in the butt as large as a plate; a blue handkerchief tied round his throat in a sailor's knot, and the collar of his shirt turned carefully over it. He had, moreover, a tolerable idea of his very correct appearance, and wore Woodstock gloves.

The trappers looked at them from head to foot, and the more they looked, the less could they make them out.

" H—!" exclaimed La Bonté emphatically.

" This beats grainin' bull-hide slick," broke from Killbuck as the strangers reined up at the fire, the younger dismounting, and staring with wonder at the weather-beaten trappers.

" Well, my men, how are you?" he rattled out. "Any game here? By Jove!" he suddenly exclaimed, seizing his rifle, as at that moment a large buzzard, the most unclean of birds, flew into the topmost branch of a cottonwood, and sat, a tempt-

ing shot. " By Jove, there's a chance !" cried the
mighty hunter ; and, bending low, started off to
approach the unwary bird in the most approved
fashion of northern deer-stalkers. The buzzard
sat quietly, and now and then stretched its neck to
gaze upon the advancing sportsman, who on such
occasions threw himself flat on the ground, and
remained motionless, in dread of alarming the bird.
It was worth while to look at the countenance of
old Killbuck, as he watched the antics of the
" bourgeois" hunter. He thought at first that the
dandy rifleman had really discovered game in the
bottom, and was nothing loth that there was a
chance of his seeing meat ; but when he understood
the object of such manœuvres, and saw the quarry
the hunter was so carefully approaching, his mouth
grinned from ear to ear, and, turning to La Bonté,
he said, " Wagh ! *he's* some—*he* is !"

Nothing doubting, however, the stranger approached the tree on which the bird was sitting,
and, getting well under it, raised his rifle and fired.
Down tumbled the bird ; and the successful hunter,
with a loud shout, rushed frantically towards it,
and bore it in triumph to the camp, earning the
most sovereign contempt from the two trappers by
the achievement.

The other stranger was a quieter character. He,
too, smiled as he witnessed the exultation of his
younger companion, (whose horse, by the way, was
scampering about the plain), and spoke kindly to

the mountaineers, whose appearance was clear evidence of the sufferings they had endured. The snakes by this time were cooked, and the trappers gave their new acquaintances the never-failing invitation to " sit and eat." When the latter, however, understood what the viands were, their looks expressed the horror and disgust they felt.

" Good God!" exclaimed the elder, " you surely cannot eat such disgusting food ? "

" This niggur doesn't savy what disgustin is," gruffly answered Killbuck; " but them as carries empty paunch three days an' more, is glad to get ' snake-meat,' I'm thinkin."

" What! you've no ammunition, then ? "

" *Well*, we haven't."

" Wait till the waggons come up, and throw away that abominable stuff, and you shall have something better, I promise," said the elder of the strangers.

" Yes," continued the younger, " some hot preserved soup, hotch-potch, and a glass of porter, will do you good."

The trappers looked at the speaker, who was talking Greek (to them). They thought the bourgeois were making fun, and did not half like it, so answered simply, " Wagh! h—'s full of hosh-posh and porter."

Two large waggons presently came up, escorted by some eight or ten stout Missourians. Sublette was amongst the number, well known as a mountain

trader, and under whose guidance the present party,
which formed a pleasure expedition at the expense
of a Scotch sportsman, was leisurely making its
way across the mountains to the Columbia.   As
several mountaineers were in company, Killbuck
and La Bonté recognised more than one friend, and
the former and Sublette were old compañeros.   As
soon as the animals were unhitched, and camp
formed on the banks of the creek, a black cook set
about preparing a meal.   Our two trapping friends
looked on with astonishment as the sable function-
ary drew from the waggon the different articles he
required to furnish forth a feed.   Hams, tongues,
tins of preserved meats, bottles of pickles, of porter,
brandy, coffee, sugar, flour, were tumbled promis-
cuously on the prairie; whilst pots and pans, knives,
forks, spoons, plates, &c. &c., displayed their unfa-
miliar faces to the mountaineers.   " Hosh-posh and
porter" did not now appear such Utopian articles
as they had first imagined; but no one but those
who have fared for years on simple meat and
water, can understand the relish with which they
accepted the invitation of the Capen (as they called
the Scotchman) to " take a horn of liquor."   Killbuck and La Bonté sat in the same position as when
we first surprised them asleep under the shadow of
Independence Rock, regarding the profuse display
of comestibles with scarce-believing eyes, and child-
ishly helpless from the novelty of the scene.   Each
took the proffered half-pint cup, filled to the brim

with excellent brandy—(no tee-totallers they !)—
looked once at the amber-coloured surface, and with
the usual mountain pledge of "here's luck !" tossed
off the grateful liquour at a breath.   This prepared
them in some measure for what was yet in store for
them.   The Scotchman bestirred the cook in his
work, and soon sundry steaming pots were lifted
from the fire, and the skillets emptied of their bread
—the contents of the former poured in large flat
pans, while panikins were filled with smoking coffee.   The two trappers needed no second invitation,
but, seizing each a panful of steaming stew, drew
the butcher-knives from their belts, and fell to
lustily—the hospitable Scotchman plying them with
more and more, and administering corrective nog-
gins of brandy the while ; until at last they were
fain to cry enough, wiped their knives on the grass,
and placed them in their sheaths—a sign that
human nature could no more.   How can pen
describe the luxury of the smoke that followed, to
lips which had not kissed pipe for many months,
and how the fragrant honey-dew from Old Virginia
was relishingly puffed.

But the Scotchman's bounty did not stop here.
He soon elicited from the lips of the hunters the
narrative of their losses and privations, and learned
that they now, without ammunition and scarcely
clothed, were on their way to Platte Fort, to hire
themselves to the Indian traders in order to earn
another outfit, wherewith once more to betake them-

selves to their perilous employment of trapping. What was their astonishment to see their entertainer presently lay out upon the ground two piles of goods, each consisting of a four-point Mackinaw, two tin canisters of powder, with corresponding lead and flints, a pair of moccasins, a shirt, and sufficient buckskin to make a pair of pantaloons; and how much the more was the wonder increased when two excellent Indian horses were presently lassoed from the cavallada, and with mountain saddle, bridle, and lariats complete, together with the two piles of goods described, presented to them " on the prairie" or " gift-free," by the kind-hearted stranger, who would not even listen to thanks for the most timely and invaluable present.

Once more equipped, our two hunters, filled with good brandy and fat buffalo meat, again wended on their way; their late entertainers continuing their pleasure trip across the gap of the South Pass, intending to visit the Great Salt Lake, or Timponogos, of the West. The former were bound for the North Fork of the Platte, with the intention of joining one of the numerous trapping parties which rendezvous at the American Fur Company's post on that branch of the river. On a fork of Sweet Water, however, not two days after the meeting with the Scotchman's waggons, they encountered a band of a dozen mountaineers, mounted on fine horses, and well armed and equipped, travelling along without the usual accompaniment of a mulada of pack-animals, two or three mules alone being packed with meat and spare ammunition. The band was proceeding at a smart rate, the horses moving with the gait peculiar to American animals, known as "*pacing*" or "*racking*," in Indian file— each of the mountaineers with a long heavy rifle resting across the horn of his saddle. Amongst them our two friends recognised Markhead, who had been of the party dispersed months before by the Blackfeet on one of the head streams of the Yellow Stone, which event had been the origin of the dire sufferings of Killbuck and La Bonté. Markhead, after running the gauntlet of numerous Indians, through the midst of whose country he passed with his usual temerity and utter disregard to danger, suffering hunger, thirst, and cold—those every-day experiences of mountain life—riddled with balls, but with three scalps hanging from his belt, made his way to a rendezvous on Bear River, whence he struck out for the Platte in early spring, in time to join the band he now accompanied, who were on a horse-stealing expedition to the Missions of Upper California. Little persuasion did either Killbuck or La Bonté require to join the sturdy freebooters. In five minutes they had gone "files-about," and at sundown were camping on the well-timbered bottom of "Little Sandy," feasting once more on delicate hump-rib and tender loin.

For California, ho!

Fourteen good rifles in the hands of fourteen

mountain men, stout and true, on fourteen strong
horses, of true Indian blood and training—fourteen
cool heads, with fourteen pairs of keen eyes in them,
each head crafty as an Indian's, directing a right
arm strong as steel, and a heart as brave as grizzly
bear's.   Before them a thousand miles of dreary
desert or wilderness, overrun by hostile savages,
thirsting for the white man's blood; famine and
drought, the arrows of wily hordes of Indians—
and, these dangers past, the invasion of the civilised
settlements of whites, the least numerous of which
contained ten times their number of armed and bitter enemies,—the sudden swoop upon their countless
herds of mules and horses, the fierce attack and
bloody slaughter ;—such were the consequences of
the expedition these bold mountaineers were now
engaged in.   Fourteen lives of any fourteen enemies
who would be rash enough to stay them, were, any
day you will, carried in the rifle barrels of these
stout fellows; who, in all the proud consciousness
of their physical qualities, neither thought, nor
cared to think, of future perils; and rode merrily
on their way, rejoicing in the dangers they must
necessarily meet.   Never a more daring band crossed the mountains ; a more than ordinary want of
caution characterised their march, and dangers were
recklessly and needlessly invited, which even the
older and more cold-blooded mountaineers seemed
not to care to avoid.   They had, each and all, many
a debt to pay the marauding Indians.   Grudges for

many privations, for wounds and loss of comrades,
rankled in their breasts; and not one but had suffered more or less in property and person at the
hands of the savages, within a few short months.
Threats of vengeance on every Redskin they met
were loud and deep; and the wild war-songs round
their nightly camp-fires, and grotesque scalp-dances,
borrowed from the Indians, proved to the initiated
that they were, one and all, "half-froze for hair."
Soon after Killbuck and La Bonté joined them, they
one day suddenly surprised a band of twenty Sioux,
scattered on a small prairie and butchering some
buffalo they had just killed. Before they could
escape, the whites were upon them with loud shouts,
and in three minutes the scalps of eleven were
dangling from their saddle-horns.

Struggling up mountains, slipping down preci-
pices, dashing over prairies which resounded with
their Indian songs, charging the Indians wherever
they met them, and without regard to their numbers; frightening with their lusty war-whoops the
miserable Diggers, who were not unfrequently surprised while gathering roots in the mountain plains,
and who, scrambling up the rocks and concealing
themselves, like sage rabbits, in holes and corners,
peered, chattering with fear, as the wild and noisy
troop rode by :—scarce drawing rein, they passed
rapidly the heads of Green and Grand Rivers,
through a country abounding in game and in excellent pasture; encountering in the upland valleys,

through which meandered the well-timbered creeks
on which they made their daily camps, many a
band of Yutas, through whom they dashed at random, caring not whether they were friends or foes.
Passing many other heads of streams, they struck
at last the edge of the desert, lying along the south-
eastern base of the Great Salt Lake, and which extends in almost unbroken sterility to the foot of the
range of the Sierra Nevada—a mountain chain,
capped with perpetual snow, that bounds the
northern extremity of a singular tract of country,
walled by mountains and utterly desert, whose salt
lagoons and lakes, although fed by many streams,
find no outlet to the ocean, but are absorbed in the
spongy soil or thirsty sand, which characterise the
different portions of this deserted tract. In the
" Grand Basin," it is reported, neither human nor
animal life can be supported. No oases cheer the
wanderer in the unbroken solitude of the vast
wilderness. More than once the lone trapper has
penetrated, with hardy enterprise, into the salt
plains of the basin; but no signs of beaver or fur-
bearing animal rewarded the attempt. The ground
is scantily covered with coarse unwholesome grass
that mules and horses refuse to eat; and the water
of the springs, impregnated with the impurities of
the soil through which it percolates, affords but
nauseating draughts to the thirsty traveller.

In passing from the more fertile uplands to the
lower plains, as they descended the streams, the

timber on their banks became scarcer, and the
groves more scattered.   The rich buffalo or *grama*
grass was exchanged for a coarser species, on which
the hard-worked animals soon grew poor and weak.
The thickets of plum and cherry, of boxalder and
quaking ash, which had hitherto fringed the creeks,
and where the deer and bear loved to resort—the
former to browse on the leaves and tender shoots,
the latter to devour the fruit—now entirely disappeared, and the only shrub seen was the eternal
sage-bush, which flourishes every where in the
western regions in uncongenial soils where other
vegetation refuses to grow.   The visible change in
the scenery had also a sensible effect on the spirits
of the mountaineers.   They travelled on in silence
through the deserted plains ; the hi-hi-hiya of their
Indian chants was no longer heard enlivening the
line of march.   More than once a Digger of the Piyutah tribe took himself and hair, in safety, from
their path, and almost unnoticed; but as they
advanced they became more cautious in their movements, and testified, by the vigilant watch they
kept, that they anticipated hostile attacks even in
these arid wastes.   They had passed without moles-
tation through the country infested by the bolder
Indians.   The mountain Yutas, not relishing the
appearance of the hunters, had left them unmolested ; but they were now entering a country inhabited
by the most degraded and abject of the western
tribes ; who, nevertheless, ever suffering from the

extremities of hunger, have their brutish wits
sharpened by the necessity of procuring food, and
rarely fail to levy a contribution of rations, of horse
or mule flesh, on the passenger in their inhospitable
country. The brutish cunning and animal instinct
of these wretches is such, that although arrant
cowards, their attacks are more feared than those
of bolder Indians. These people—called the Yam-
paricas or Root-Diggers—are, nevertheless, the
degenerate descendants of those tribes which once
overran that portion of the continent of North
America now comprehended within the boundaries
of Mexico, and who have left such startling evidences
in their track of a comparatively superior state of
civilisation. They now form an outcast tribe of the
great nation of the Apache, which extends under
various names from the Great Salt Lake along the
table-lands on each side the Sierra Madre to the
tropic of Cancer, where they merge into what are
called the Mexican Indians. The whole of this
nation is characterised by most abject cowardice ;
and they even refuse to meet the helpless Mexicans
in open fight—unlike the Yuta or Camanche, who
carry bold and open warfare into the territories of
their civilised enemy, and never shrink from hand
to hand encounter. The Apaches and the degenerate Diggers pursue a cowardly warfare, hiding in
ambush, and shooting the passer-by with arrows ;
or, dashing upon him at night when steeped in sleep,
they bury their arrow to the feather in his heaving

breast. As the Mexicans say, "*Sin ventaja, no salen;*" they never attack without odds. But they are not the less dangerous enemies on this account; and by the small bands of trappers who visit their country, they are the more dreaded by reason of this cowardly and wolfish system of warfare.

To provide against surprise, therefore, as the hunters rode along, flankers were extended *en guerilla* on each side, mounting the high points to reconnoitre the country, and keeping a sharp look-out for Indian sign. At night the animals were securely hobbled, and a horse-guard posted round them—a service of great danger, as the stealthy cat-like Diggers are often known to steal up silently, under cover of the darkness, towards the sentinel, shoot him with their arrows, and approaching the animals, cut the hobbles and drive them away unseen.

One night they encamped on a creek where was but little of the coarsest pasture, and that little scattered here and there; so that they were compelled to allow their animals to roam farther than usual from camp in search of food. Four of the hunters, however, accompanied them to guard against surprise; whilst but half of those in camp lay down to sleep, the others, with rifles in their hands, remaining prepared for any emergency. This day they had killed one of their two pack-mules for food, game not having been met with for several days; but the animal was so poor, that it

scarcely afforded more than one tolerable meal to
the whole party.

A short time before the dawn of day an alarm
was given; the animals were heard to snort violently ; a loud shout was heard, followed by the
sharp crack of a rifle, and the tramp of galloping
horses plainly showed that a stampede had been
effected. The whites instantly sprang to their
arms, and rushed in the direction of the sounds.
The body of the cavallada, however, had luckily
turned, and, being headed by the mountaineers,
were surrounded and secured, with the loss of only
three, which had probably been mounted by the
Indians.

Day breaking soon after, one of their band was
discovered to be missing ; and it was then found
that a man who had been standing horse-guard at
the time of the attack, had not come into camp with
his companions. At that moment a thin spiral
column of smoke was seen to rise from the banks
of the creek, telling but too surely the fate of the
missing mountaineer. It was the signal of the
Indians to their people that a "coup" had been
struck, and that an enemy's scalp remained in their
triumphant hands,

" H——! " exclaimed the trappers in a breath ;
and soon imprecations and threats of revenge, loud
and deep, were showered upon the heads of the
treacherous Indians. Some of the party rushed to
the spot where the guard had stood, and there lay

the body of their comrade, pierced with lance and
arrow, the scalp gone, and the body otherwise
mutilated in a barbarous manner. Five were
quickly in the saddle, mounted upon the strongest
horses, and flying along the track of the Indians,
who had made off towards the mountains with their
prize and booty. We will not follow them in their
work of bloody vengeance, save by saying that they
followed the savages to their village, into which
they charged headlong, recovered their stolen
horses, and returned to camp at sundown with
thirteen scalps dangling from their rifles, in payment for the loss of their unfortunate companion.*

In their further advance, hunger and thirst were
their daily companions; they were compelled to
kill several of their animals for food, but were fortunate enough to replace them by a stroke of good
luck in meeting a party of Indians returning from
an excursion against one of the Californian settlements with a tolerably large band of horses. Our
hunters met this band one fine morning, and dashed
into the midst at once ; half a dozen Indians bit the
dust, and twenty horses were turned over from red

---

* In Frémont's expedition to California, on a somewhat simi-
lar occasion, two mountaineers, one the celebrated Kit Carson,
the other a St Louis Frenchman named Godey, and both old
trappers, performed a feat surpassing the one described above,
inasmuch as they were but two. They charged into an Indian village to rescue some stolen horses, and avenge the slaughter of
two New Mexicans who had been butchered by the Indians ;
both which objects they effected, returning to camp with the lost
animals and a couple of propitiatory scalps.

to white masters in as many seconds, which re-
mounted those whose animals had been eaten, and
enabled the others to exchange their worn-out
steeds for fresh ones. This fortunate event was
considered a *coup*, and the event was celebrated by
the slaughter of a fat young horse, which furnished an excellent supper that night—a memorable
event in these starveling regions.

They were now devouring their horses and mules
at the rate of one every alternate day ; for, so poor
were the animals, that one scarcely furnished an
ample meal for the thirteen hungry hunters. They
were once more reduced to the animals they rode
on ; and after a fast of twenty-four hours' duration,
were debating on the propriety of drawing lots as
to whose Rosinante should fill the kettle, when some
Indians suddenly appeared making signs of peace
upon the bluff, and indicating a disposition to enter
the camp for the purpose of trading   Being invited to approach, they offered to trade a few
dressed elk-skins ; but being asked for meat, they
said that their village was a long way off, and
they had nothing with them but a small portion of
some game they had lately killed. When requested
to produce this, they hesitated, but the trappers
looking hungry and angry at the same moment, an
old Indian drew from under his blanket several
flaps of portable dried meat, which he declared was
bear's. It was but a small ration amongst so many ;
but, being divided, was quickly laid upon the fire

to broil. The meat was stringy, and of whitish colour, altogether unlike any flesh the trappers had before eaten. Killbuck was the first to discover this. He had been quietly masticating the last mouthful of his portion, the stringiness of which required more than usual dental exertion, when the novelty of the flavour struck him as something singular. Suddenly his jaws ceased their work, he thought a moment, took the morsel from his mouth, looked at it intently, and dashed it into the fire.

" Man-meat, by G—! " he cried out; and at the words every jaw stopped work: the trappers looked at the meat and each other.

" I'm dog-gone if it ain't! " cried old Walker, looking at his piece, " and white meat at that, wagh! " (and report said it was not the first time he had tasted such viands;) and the conviction seizing each mind, every mouthful was quickly spat into the fire, and the ire of the deceived whites was instantly turned upon the luckless providers of the feast. They saw the storm that was brewing, and without more ado turned tail from the camp, and scuttled up the bluffs, where, turning round, they fired a volley of arrows at the tricked mountaineers, and instantly disappeared.

However, the desert and its nomade pilferers were at length passed; the sandy plains became grass-covered prairies; the monstrous cottonwood on the creeks was replaced by oak and ash; the

surface of the country grew more undulating, and
less broken up into cañons and ravines; elk and
deer leaped in the bottoms, and bands of antelope
dotted the plains, with occasional troops of wild
horses, too wary to allow the approach of man.
On the banks of a picturesque stream called the
San Joaquim, the party halted a few days to recruit
themselves and animals, feasting the while on the
fattest of venison and other game. They then
struck to the south-east for two days, until they
reached a branch of the " Las Animas," a clear
stream running through a pretty valley, well
timbered and abounding in game. Here, as they
wound along the river-banks, a horseman suddenly
appeared upon the bluff above them, galloping at
a furious rate along the edge. His dress approached in some degree to civilised attire. A
broad-brimmed sombrero surmounted his swarthy
face ; a coloured blanket, through a slit in which
his head was thrust, floated in the air from his
shoulders ; leathern leggings encased his lower
limbs; and huge spurs jingled on his heels. He
rode in a high-peaked Mexican saddle, his feet
thrust in ponderous stirrups, and in his hand swung
a coil of ready lasso, his only offensive arm. One
of the trappers knew a little Spanish, and instantly
hailed him.

" *Compadre,*" he shouted, " *por onde va ?* " The
Californian reined in suddenly, throwing the horse
he rode on its very haunches, and darting down the

bluff, galloped unhesitatingly into the midst of the hunters.

"*Americanos!*" he exclaimed, glancing at them ; and continued, smiling—"*Y caballos quieren, por eso vienen tan lejitos. Jesus, que mala gente!*"— " It's horses you want, and for this you come all this way. Ah, what rogues you are !"

He was an Indian, employed at the mission of San Fernando, distant three days' journey from their present position, and was now searching for a band of horses and mules which had strayed. San Fernando, it appeared, had once before been visited by a party of mountain free-booters, and the Indian therefore divined the object of the present one. He was, he told them, " *un Indio, pero mansito :*" an Indian, but a tame one ;* " *de mas, Christiano :*" a Christian moreover (exhibiting a small cross which hung round his neck). There were many people about the mission, he said, who knew how to fight, and had plenty of arms ; and there were enough to " eat up" the " *Americanos, sin frijoles,*" without beans, as he facetiously observed. For his part, however, he was very friendly to the *Americanos ;* he had once met a man of that nation who was a good sort of fellow, and had made him a present of tobacco, of which he was particularly fond. Finding this hint did not take, he said that the horses and mules belonging to the mission were innumer-

* The Mexicans call the Indians living near the missions and engaged in agriculture, *mansos,* or *mansitos,* tame.

able—" like that," he added, sweeping his hand to
all points of the compass over the plain, to intimate
that they would cover that extent; and he could
point out a large herd grazing nearer at hand than
the mission, and guarded but by three *vaqueros*.
Regaled with venison, and with a smoke of his coveted tobacco, he rode off, and made his way to the
mission without delay, conveying the startling intelligence that a thousand Americans were upon them.

The next morning the thirteen doughty mountaineers quietly resumed their journey, moving
leisurely along towards the object of their expedition.

It will not be out of place here to digress a little,
in order to describe the singular features of the
establishments formed in those remote regions by
the Catholic church, as nuclei round which to con-
centrate the wandering tribes that inhabit the country, with a view to give them the benefit of civilised
example, and to wean them from their restless no-
madic habits.

The establishment of missions in Upper California
is coeval with the first settlement of Southern Mexico.
No sooner had Spanish rule taken a firm foothold
in the Aztec empire, than the avowed primary object of the military expedition began to be carried
into effect. " To save the souls" of the savage and
barbarous subjects of their most Catholic majesties
was ever inculcated upon the governors of the con-
quered country as the grand object to be sought

after, as soon as tranquillity was partially restored
by the submission of the Mexicans ; and the Cross,
the sacred emblem of the Catholic faith, was to be
upraised in the remotest corners of the country, and
the natives instructed and compelled to worship it,
in lieu of the grotesque images of their own idola-
trous religion.

To carry into effect these orthodox instructions,
troops of pious priests, of friars and monks of every
order, and even of saintly nuns, followed in the wake
of the victorious armies of Cortez ; and, girding up
their loins with zealous fervour and enthusiasm, and
with an enterprise and hardihood worthy of bucca-
neers, they pushed their adventurous way far into
the bowels of the land, preaching devoutly and with
commendable perseverance to savages who did not
understand a syllable of what they so eloquently
discoursed ; and returning, after the lapse of many
months passed in this first attempt, with glowing
accounts of the " *muy buen indole*," the very ductile
disposition of the savages, and of the thousands they
had converted to " *la santa fé catolica.*"

Ferdinand and Isabel, of glorious memory, at
once beat up for volunteers. Crowds of Franciscan
monks, greasy Capuchinos, and nuns of orthodox
odour, joined the band ; and saints even of the
feminine gender, long since canonised and up aloft
amongst the goodly muster of saints and martyrs,
put foot once more on *terra firma*, and, rosary in
hand, crossed the seas to participate in the good

work. As proof of this latter fact, one Venabides, a Franciscan, whose veracity is beyond impeachment, declared that, while preaching in the regions now known as New Mexico, one million Indians from the " rumbo" known as Cibolo, a mighty nation, approached his temporary pulpit on the Rio Grande, and requested in a body the favour of being baptised. Struck with the singularity of this request from Indians with whom he had as yet held no communication, and with conscientious scruple as to whether he would be justified in performing such ceremony without their having received previous instruction, he hesitated a few moments before making an answer. At this juncture the Indians espied a medallion which hung around his neck, bearing the effigy of a certain saint of extraordinary virtúe. At sight of this they fell on their knees before it ; and it was some time before they found words (in what language does not appear) to explain to the holy father that the original of that effigy, which hung pendant from his neck, had been long amongst them instructing them in the elements of the Christian religion, and had only lately disappeared ; informing them that certain reverend men would shortly appear in the land, who would finish the good work she had devoutly commenced, and clench the business by baptising the one million miserable sinners who now knelt before El Padre Venabides.

" Valgame Dios !" reverently exclaimed that worthy man, " qui milagro es este ;" [what a mi-

racle is this I hear ;] and casting up his eyes, and
speaking slowly, as if he weighed every word, and
taxing his memory of the historical calendar of
saints, continued,—

" *Se murió—aquella—santissima—muger—en el
ano 175—es decir—ya hacen—mil—quatro—cien-
tos—anos.*" [That most holy woman died in the
year 175, that is to say, one thousand four hundred
years ago.]

" Oh, what a strange thing is this!" the padre
continues devoutly. " After so many ages spent in
heaven in company of the angels, of most holy men,
and of virgins the most pure ; and, perhaps, also in
the company of my worthy and esteemed friend and
patron, Don Vincente Carvajal y Calvo, who died a
few years ago in San Lucar of Xeres (bequeathing
me certain arrobas of dry wine, of a class I greatly
esteem—for which act he deserved to be canonised,
and, I have no doubt, is), the said Don Vincente
Carvajal y Calvo being, moreover, a man of the
purest and holiest thoughts (Dios mio ! what a
puchero that man always had on his table !) this
holy woman comes here—to these wild and remote
regions ; this holy woman (who died fifteen hundred
years ago), abandoning the company of angels, of
holy men, and sanctified women and virgins, and
also of Don Vincente Carvajal y Calvo (that worthy
man !)—comes here, I say, where there are neither
pucheros, nor garbanzos, nor dry wine, nor sweet
wine, neither of Xeres, nor of Val de Peñas, nor of

Peralta; where" (sobbed the padre, and bellowed the last word) " there is—nothing either to eat or to drink. Valgame Purissima Maria! And what is the name of this holy woman? the world will ask," continues Venabides. " Santa Clara of Carmona is her name, one well known in my native country, who leaves heaven and all its joys, wends her way to the distant wilds of New Spain, and spends years in inducting the savage people to the holy faith. Truly a pious work, and pleasing to God!" *

Thus spoke Venabides the Franciscan, and no doubt he believed what he said; and many others in Old Spain were fools enough to believe it too, for the shaven heads flocked over in greater numbers, and the cry was ever " still they come."

Along the whole extent of the table-lands, not an Indian tribe but was speedily visited by the preaching friars and monks; and, in less than a century after the conquest of Mexico by the Spaniards, these hardy and enthusiastic frayles had pushed their way into the inhospitable regions of New Mexico, nearly two thousand miles distant from the valley of Anahuac. How they succeeded in surmounting the natural obstacles presented by the wild and barren deserts they traversed; how they escaped the infinite peril they encountered at every step, at the hands of the savage inhabitants of the

* From a manuscript obtained in Santa Fé of New Mexico, describing the labours of the missionaries Fray Augustin Ruiz, Venabides, and Marcos, in the year 1585.

o

country, with whose language they were totally
unacquainted, is sufficient puzzle to those who, in
the present day, have attempted a journey in the
same regions.

However, it is imposssible not to admire the
hardihood of these holy pioneers of civilisation,
who, totally unfitted by their former mode of life
for undergoing such hardships as they must have
anticipated, threw themselves into the wilderness
with fearless and stubborn zeal.

For the most part, however, they found the
Indians exceedingly hospitable and well disposed;
and it was not until some time after—when, receiving from the missionary monks glowing, and not
always very truthful accounts of the riches of the
country in which they had located themselves, the
governors of Mexico despatched armed expeditions
under adventurous desperadoes to take and retain
possession of the said country, with orders to com-
pel the submission of the native tribes, and enforce
their obedience to the authority of the whites—that
the simple and confiding Indians began to see the
folly they had committed in permitting the resi-
dence amongst them of these superior beings, whom
they had first looked upon as more than mortal,
but who, when strong enough to do so, were not
long in throwing off the mask, and proving to the
simple savages that they were much " more human
than divine."

Thus, in the province of New Mexico, Fray

Augustin Ruiz, with his co-preachers, Marcos and Venabides, were kindly received by the native inhabitants, and we have seen how one million (?) Indians came from the "rumbo" of the Cibolo. ready and willing to receive the baptismal sacrament. This Cibolo, or Sivulo, as it is written in some old MSS., is, by the way, mysteriously alluded to by the monkish historians who have written on this region, as being a kingdom inhabited by a very superior class of Indians to any met with between Anahuac and the Vale of Taos—in the enjoyment of a high state of civilisation, inhabiting a well-built city, the houses of which were three stories high, and having attained considerable perfection in the domestic arts. This, notwithstanding the authority of Don Francisco Vasquez Coronado, who visited Cibolo, and of Solis and Venegas, who have guaranteed the assertion, must be received *cum grano salis;* but, at all events, the civilisation of the mysterious Cibolo may be compared to that of the Aztec empire, under Montezuma, at the time of the Spanish Conquest, both being egregiously exaggerated by the historians of the day. Cibolo was situated on a river called Tegue. At this day, neither name is known to the inhabitants of New Mexico. If pate-shaven Venabides had held his tongue, New Mexico might now be in the peaceful possession of the Catholic Missions, and the property of the Church of Mexico pretty considerably enhanced by the valuable *placeres,* or gold wash-ings, which abound in that province. Full, however, of the wonderful miracle of Santa Clara of Carmona, which had been brought to light through the agency of the medallion at the end of his rosario, Fray Venabides must needs return to Spain, and humbug poor old Fernando, and even the more sensible Isabel, with wonderful accounts of the riches of the country he had been instrumental in exploring, and of the excellent disposition of the natives to receive the word of God. Don Juan Oñate was, therefore, quickly despatched to take possession; and in his train followed twelve Castilian families of *sangre azul,* to colonise the newly-acquired territory. The names of these still remain, disgraced by the degenerate wretches who now bear them, but in whom scarce a drop of blood remains which ever filtered from the veins of the paladins of Old Castile.

Then commenced the troublous times. The missions were upheld by dint of steel alone; and frequently the Indians rose, and often massacred their white persecutors. The colonists were more than once driven bodily from New Mexico, and were only reinstated by the aid of large bodies of armed men.

In California, however, they managed these things better. The wily monks took care to keep all interlopers from the country, established themselves in snug quarters, instructed the Indians in agriculture, and soon gained such an ascendancy over them, that no difficulty was experienced in keeping them under proper and wholesome restraint. Strong and commodious missions were built and fortified, well stored with arms and ammunition, and containing sufficient defenders to defy attack. Luxuriant gardens and thriving vineyards soon surrounded these isolated stations : the plains waved with golden corn ; whilst domestic cattle, thriving on the rich pasture, and roaming far and near, multiplied and increased a hundred-fold.

Nothing can be more beautiful than the appearance of one of these missions, to the traveller who has lately passed the arid and barren wilderness of the North-west. The *adobe* walls of the convent-looking building, surmounted by cross and belfry, are generally hidden in a mass of luxuriant vegetation. Fig-trees, bananas, cherry, and apple, leaf-spreading platanos, and groves of olives, form umbrageous vistas, under which the sleek monks delight to wander ; gardens, cultivated by their own hands, testify to the horticultural skill of the worthy padres ; whilst vineyards yield their grateful produce to gladden the hearts of the holy exiles in these western solitudes. Vast herds of cattle roam half-wild on the plains, and bands of mules and horses, whose fame has even reached the distant table-lands of the Rocky Mountains, and excited the covetousness of the hunters—and thousands of which, from the day they are foaled to that of their death, never feel a saddle on their backs—cover

the country. Indians (Mansitos) idle round the
skirts of these vast herds (whose very numbers
keep them together), living, at their own choice,
upon the flesh of mule, or ox, or horse.

CHAPTER VII.

The Mission of San Fernando is situated on a small river called Las Animas, a branch of the Los Martires. The convent is built at the neck of a large plain, at the point of influx of the stream from the broken spurs of the sierra. The savana is covered with luxuriant grass, kept down, however, by the countless herds of cattle which pasture on it. The banks of the creek are covered with a lofty growth of oak and poplar, which near the Mission have been considerably thinned for the purpose of affording fuel and building materials for the increasing settlement. The convent stands in the midst of a grove of fruit-trees, its rude tower and cross peeping above them, and contrasting picturesquely with the wildness of the surrounding scenery. Gardens and orchards lie immediately in front of the building, and a vineyard stretches away to the upland ridge of the valley. The huts of the Indians are scattered here and there, built of stone and adobe, sometimes thatched with flags and boughs, but comfortable enough. The convent itself is a substantial building, of the style of architecture characterising monastic edifices in most parts of the

world. Loopholes peer from its plastered walls, and
on a flat portion of the roof a comically mounted
gingall or wall-piece, carrying a two-pound ball,
threatens the assailant in time of war. At one end
of the oblong building, a rough irregular arch of
sun-burned bricks is surmounted by a rude cross,
under which hangs a small but deep-toned bell—
the wonder of the Indian peones, and highly vene-
rated by the frayles themselves, who received it as
a present from a certain venerable archbishop of
Old Spain, and who, whilst guarding it with reverential awe, tell wondrous tales of its adventures on
the road to its present abiding place.

Of late years the number of the canonical inmates
of the convent has been much reduced—there being
but four priests now to do the duties of the eleven
who formerly inhabited it : Fray Augustin, a Capuchin of due capacity of paunch, being at the head
of the holy quartette. Augustin is the conventual
name of the reverend father, who fails not to im-
press upon such casual visitants to that *ultima Thule*
as he deems likely to appreciate the information,
that, but for his humility, he might add the sonorous
appellations of Ignacio Sabanal-Morales-y Fuentes—
his family being of the best blood of Old Castile,
and known there since the days of Ruy Gomez —el
Campéador—possessing, moreover, half the " vega "
of the Ebro, &c., where, had fate been propitious,
he would now have been the sleek superior of a rich

capuchin convent, instead of vegetating, a leather-clad frayle, in the wilds of California Alta.

Nevertheless, his lot is no bad one. With plenty of the best and fattest meat to eat, whether of beef or venison, of bear or mountain mutton ; with good wine and brandy of home make, and plenty of it ; fruit of all climes in great abundance ; wheaten or corn bread to suit his palate ; a tractable flock of natives to guide, and assisted in the task by three brother shepherds ; far from the strife of politics or party—secure from hostile attack (not quite, by-the-by), and eating, drinking, and sleeping away his time, one would think that Fray Augustin Ignacio Sabanal-Morales-y Fuentes had little to trouble him, and had no cause to regret even the vega of Castilian Ebro, held by his family since the days of el Campéador.

One evening Fray Augustin sat upon an adobe bench, under the fig-tree shadowing the porch of the Mission. He was dressed in a goat-skin jerkin, softly and beautifully dressed, and descending to his hips, under which his only covering—tell it not in Gath !—was a long linen shirt, reaching to his knees, and lately procured from Puebla de los Angeles, as a sacerdotal garment. Boots, stockings, or unmentionables, he had none. A cigarito, of tobacco rolled in corn shuck, was occasionally placed between his lips ; whereupon huge clouds of smoke rushed in columns from his mouth and nostrils.

His face was of a golden yellow colour, relieved by
arched and very black eyebrows ; his shaven chin
was of most respectable duplicity—his corporation
of orthodox dimensions. Several Indians and half-
bred Mexican women were pounding Indian corn
on metates near at hand ; whilst sundry beef-fed
urchins of whitey-brown complexion sported before
the door, exhibiting, as they passed Fray Augustin,
a curious resemblance to the strongly marked
features of that worthy padre. They were probably his nieces and nephews—a class of relations
often possessed in numbers by priests and monks.

The three remaining brothers were absent from
the Mission ; Fray Bernardo, hunting elk in the
sierra ; Fray José, gallivanting at Puebla de los
Angeles, ten days' journey distant ; Fray Cristoval,
lassoing colts upon the plain. Augustin, thus left
to his own resources, had just eaten his vespertine
frijolitos and chile colorado, and was enjoying a
post-cœnal smoke of fragrant pouche under the
shadow of his own fig-tree.

Whilst thus employed, an Indian dressed in Mexican attire approached him hat in hand, and, making
a reverential bow, asked his directions concerning
domestic business of the Mission.

" Hola ! friend José," cried Fray Augustin in a
thick guttural voice, " pensaba yo—I was thinking
that it was very nearly this time three years ago
when those ' malditos Americanos' came by here
and ran off with so many of our cavallada."

" True, reverend father," answered the administrador, " just three years ago, all but fifteen days :
I remember it well. *Malditos sean*—curse them !"

" How many did we kill, José ?"

" Quizas mōōchos—a great many, I dare say.
But they did not fight fairly—charged right upon
us, and gave us no time to do any thing. They
don't know how to fight, these Mericanos ; come
right at you, before you can swing a lasso, halloo-
ing like Indios Bravos."

" But, José, how many did they leave dead on
the field ?"

" Not one."

" And we ?"

" Valgame Dios ! thirteen dead, and ·many more
wounded."

" That's it ! Now if these savages come again
(and the Chemeguaba, who came in yesterday,
says he saw a large trail), we must fight adentro—
within—outside is no go ; for as you very pro-
perly say, José, these Americans don't know how to
fight, and kill us before—before we can kill them !
Vaya !"

At this moment there issued from the door of the
Mission Don Antonio Velez Trueba, a Gachupin—
that is, a native of Old Spain—a wizened old hidalgo
refugee, who had left the mother country on account
of his political opinions, which were stanchly Carlist,
and had found his way—how, he himself scarcely
knew—from Mexico to San Francisco in Upper Cali-

fornia, where, having a most perfect contempt for
every thing Mexican, and hearing that in the Mission of San Fernando, far away, were a couple of
Spanish padres of " sangre regular," he had started
into the wilderness to ferret them out ; and having
escaped all dangers on the route (which, however,
were hardly dangers to the Don, who could not
realise the idea of scalp-taking savages), had arrived
with a whole skin at the Mission. There he was
received with open arms by his countryman Fray
Augustin, who made him welcome to all the place
afforded, and there he harmlessly smoked away his
time ; his heart far away on the banks of the Genil
and in the grape-bearing vegas of his beloved Anda-
lusia, his withered cuerpo in the sierras of Upper
California. Don Antonio was the walking essence
of a Spaniard of the *ancien régime*. His family
dated from the Flood, and with the exception of
sundry refreshing jets of Moorish blood, injected
into the Truebas during the Moorish epoch, no
strange shoot was ever engrafted on their genea-
logical tree. The marriages of the family were
ever confined to the family itself—never looking to
fresh blood in a station immediately below it, which
was not hidalgueño ; nor above, since any thing
higher in rank than the Trueba y Trueba family,
no habia, there was not.

Thus, in the male and female scions of the house,
were plainly visible the ill effects of breeding " in
and in." The male Truebas were sadly degenerate

Dons, in body as in mind—compared to their ancestors of Boabdil's day; and the sennoritas of the
name were all eyes, and eyes alone, and hardly of
such stamp as would have tempted that amorous
monarch to bestow a kingdom for a kiss, as ancient
ballads tell.

> " Dueña de la negra toca,
> Por un beso de tu boca,
> Diera un reyno, Boabdil ;
> Y yo por ello, Cristiana,
> Te diera de buena gana
> Mil cielos, si fueran mil."

Come of such poor stock, and reared on tobacco
smoke and " gazpacho," Don Antonio would not
have shone, even amongst pigmy Mexicans, for physical beauty. Five feet high, a framework of bones
covered with a skin of Andalusian tint, the Trueba
stood erect and stiff in all the consciousness of his
" sangre regular." His features were handsome,
but entirely devoid of flesh, his upper lip was covered with a jet-black mustache mixed with gray, his
chin was bearded " like the pard." Every one
around him clad in deer and goat skin, our Don
walked conspicuous in shining suit of black—much
the worse for wear, it must be confessed—with beaver hat sadly battered, and round his body and over
his shoulder an unexceptionable " capa" of the am-
plest dimensions. Asking, as he stepped over him,
the pardon of an Indian urchin who blocked the
door, and bowing with punctilious politeness to the

sturdy mozas who were grinding corn, Don Antonio approached our friend Augustin, who was discussing warlike matters with his administrador.

" Hola! Don Antonio, how do you find yourself, sir?"

" Perfectly well, and your very humble servant, reverend father; and your worship also, I trust you are in good health?"

" *Sin novedad*—without novelty;" which, since it was one hour and a half since our friends had separated to take their siestas, was not impossible.

" Myself and the worthy José," continued Fray Augustin, " were speaking of the vile invasion of a band of North American robbers, who three years since fiercely assaulted this peaceful Mission, killing many of its inoffensive inhabitants, wounding many more, and carrying off several of our finest colts and most promising mules to their dens and caves in the Rocky Mountains. Not with impunity, however, did they effect this atrocity. José informs me that many of the assailants were killed by my brave Indians. How many said you, José?"

" Quizas mo-o-ochos," answered the Indian.

" Yes, probably a great multitude," continued the padre; " but, unwarned by such well-merited castigation, it has been reported to me by a Cheme-guaba mansito, that a band of these audacious marauders are now on the road to repeat the offence, numbering many thousands, well mounted and armed; and to oppose these white barbarians it behoves us to make every preparation of defence."*

"There is no cause for alarm," answered the Andaluz. "I (tapping his breast) have served in three wars : in that glorious one 'de la Independencia,' when our glorious patriots drove the French like sheep across the Pyrenees ; in that equally glorious one of 1821 ; and in the late magnanimous struggle for the legitimate rights of his majesty Charles V., king of Spain (doffing his hat), whom God preserve. With that right arm," cried the spirited Don, extending his shrivelled member, "I have supported the throne of my kings — have fought for my country, mowing down its enemies before me ; and with it," vehemently exclaimed the Gachupin, working himself into a perfect frenzy, "I will slay these Norte Americanos, should they dare to show their faces in my front. Adios, Don Augustin Ignacio Sabanal-Morales-y Fuentes," he cried, doffing his hat with an earth-sweeping bow ; "I go to grind my sword. Till then adieu."

"A countryman of mine!" said the frayle, admiringly, to the administrador. "With him by our side we need not to fear : neither Norte Americanos, nor the devil himself, can harm us when he is by."

---

* From the report to the Governor of California by the Head of the Mission, in reference to the attacks by the American mountaineers.

Whilst the Trueba sharpens his Tizona, and the
priest puffs volumes of smoke from his nose and
mouth, let us introduce to the reader one of the
muchachitas, who knelt grinding corn on the me-
tate, to make tortillas for the evening meal. Juanita
was a stout wench from Sonora, of Mexican blood,
hardly as dark as the other women who surrounded
her, and with a drop or two of the Old Spanish
blood struggling with the darker Indian tint to
colour her plump cheeks. An enagua (a short petticoat) of red serge was confined round her waist by
a gay band ornamented with beads, and a chemisette
covered the upper part of the body, permitting,
however, a prodigal display of her charms. Whilst
pounding sturdily at the corn, she laughed and
joked with her fellow-labourers upon the anticipated
American attack, which appeared to have but few
terrors for her. "Que vengan," she exclaimed—"let
them come; they are only men, and will not molest
us women. Besides, I have seen these white men
before—in my own country, and they are fine fellows, very tall, and as white as the snow on the
sierras. Let them come, say I!"

" Only hear the girl! " cried another : " if these
savages come, then will they kill Pedrillo, and what
will Juanita say to lose her sweetheart ?"

" Pedrillo ! " sneered the latter; " what care I
for Pedrillo? Soy Mejicana, yo—a Mexican girl
am I, I'd have you know, and don't demean me to
look at a wild Indian. Not I, indeed, by my salva-

tion! What I say is, let the Norte Americanos come."

At this juncture Fray Augustin called for a glass of aguardiente, which Juanita was despatched to bring, and, on presenting it, the churchman facetiously inquired why she wished for the Americans, adding, " Don't think they'll come here—no, no : here we are brave men, and have Don Antonio with us, a noble fellow, well used to arms." As the words were on his lips, the clattering of a horse's hoofs was heard rattling across the loose stones and pebbles in the bed of the river, and presently an Indian herder galloped up to the door of the Mission, his horse covered with foam; and its sides bleeding from spur-wounds.

" Oh, padre mio!" he cried, as soon as he caught sight of his reverence, " vienen los Americanos—the Americans, the Americans are upon us. Ave Maria purissima!—more than ten thousand are at my heels ! "

Up started the priest and shouted for the Don.

That hidalgo presently appeared, armed with the sword that had graced his thigh in so many glorious encounters—the sword with which he had mowed down the enemies of his country, and by whose aid he now proposed to annihilate the American savages, should they dare to appear before him.

The alarm was instantly given; peones, vagueros hurried from the plains ; and milpas, warned by the deep-toned bell, which soon rung out its sonorous alarum. A score of mounted Indians, armed with gun and lasso, dashed off to bring intelligence of the enemy. The old gingall on the roof was crammed with powder and bullets to the very muzzle, by the frayle's own hand. Arms were brought and piled in the sala, ready for use. The padre exhorted, the women screamed, the men grew pale and nervous, and thronged within the walls. Don Antonio, the fiery Andaluz, alone remained outside, flourishing his whetted sabre, and roaring to the padre, who stood on the roof with lighted match, by the side of his formidable cannon, not to be affrighted. " That he, the Trueba, was there, with his Tizona, ready to defeat the devil himself should he come on."

He was deaf to the entreaties of the priest to enter.

" Siempre en el frente—Ever in the van," he said, " was the war-cry of the Truebas."

But now a cloud of dust was seen approaching from the plain, and presently a score of horsemen dashed headlong towards the Mission. " El enemigo," shouted Fray Augustin; and, without waiting to aim, he clapped his match to the touch-hole of the gun, harmlessly pointed to the sky, and crying out " in el nombre de Dios "—in God's name—as he did so, was instantly knocked over and over by the recoil of the piece, then was as instantly seized by some of the Indian garrison, and forced through the trap door into the building; whilst the horsemen (who were his own scouts) galloped up with the intelligence that the enemy was at hand, and in over-whelming force.

Thereupon the men were all mounted, and formed in a body before the building, to the amount of more than fifty, well armed with guns or bows and arrows. Here the gallant Don harangued them, and infusing into their hearts a little of his own courage, they eagerly demanded to be led against the enemy. Fray Augustin re-appeared on the roof, gave them his blessing, advised them to give no quarter, and, with slight misgivings, saw them ride off to the conflict.

About a mile from the Mission, the plain gradu-ally ascended to a ridge of moderate elevation, on which was a growth of dwarf oak and ilex. To this point the eyes of the remaining inmates of the con-vent were earnestly directed, as here the enemy was first expected to make his appearance. Pre-sently a few figures were seen to crown the ridge, clearly defined against the clear evening sky. Not more than a dozen mounted men composed this party, which all imagined must be doubtless the vanguard of the thousand invaders. On the summit of the ridge they halted a few minutes, as if to re-connoitre; and by this time the Californian horse-men were halted in the plain, midway between the Mission and the ridge, and distant from the former less than half-a-mile, so that all the operations were clearly visible to the lookers-on.

The enemy wound slowly, in Indian file, down

the broken ground of the descent; but when the plain was reached, they formed into something like a line, and trotted fearlessly towards the Californians. These began to sit uneasily in their saddles; nevertheless they made a forward movement, and even broke into a gallop, but soon halted, and again huddled together. Then the mountaineers quickened their pace, and their loud shout was heard as they dashed into the middle of the faltering troop. The sharp cracks of the rifles followed, and the duller reports of the smooth-bored pieces of the Californians; a cloud of smoke and dust arose from the plain, and immediately half-a-dozen horses, with empty saddles, broke from it, followed quickly by the Californians, flying like mad across the level. The little steady line of the mountaineers advanced, and puffs of smoke arose, as they loaded and discharged their rifles at the flying horsemen. As the Americans came on, however, one was seen to totter in his saddle, the rifle fell from his grasp, and he tumbled headlong to the ground. For an instant his companions surrounded the fallen man, but again forming, dashed towards the Mission, shouting fierce war-whoops, and brandishing aloft their long and heavy rifles. Of the defeated Californians some jumped off their horses at the door of the Mission, and sought shelter within; others galloped off towards the sierra in panic-stricken plight. Before the gate, however, still paced valiantly the proud hidalgo, encumbered with his cloak, and waving

with difficulty his sword above his head. To the
priest and women, who implored him to enter, he
replied with cries of defiance, "Viva Carlos Quinto,"
and "Death or glory." He shouted in vain to the
flying crowd to halt; but, seeing their panic was
beyond hope, he clutched his weapon more firmly as
the Americans dashed at him, closed his teeth and
his eyes, thought once of the vega of his beloved
Genil, and of Granada la Florida, and gave himself
up for lost. Those inside the Mission, when they
observed the flight of their cavalry, gave up the
defence as hopeless; and already the charging
mountaineers were almost under the walls, when
they observed the curious figure of the little Don
making demonstrations of hostility.

"Wagh!" exclaimed the leading hunter (no other
than our friend La Bonté), "here's a little crittur
as means to do all the fighting;" and seizing his
rifle by the barrel, he poked at the Don with the
butt-end, who parried the blow, and with such a
sturdy stroke, as nearly severed the stock in two.
Another mountaineer rode up, and, swinging his
lasso overhead, threw the noose dexterously over
the Spaniard's head, and as it fell over his shoulders,
drew it taut, thus securing the arms of the pugnacious Don as in a vice.

"Quartel!" cried the latter; "por Dios, quartel!"

"Quarter be d——!" exclaimed one of the whites,
who understood Spanish; "who's agoin' to hurt you,
you little crittur?"

By this time Fray Augustin was waving a white
flag from the roof, in token of surrender; and soon
after he appeared trembling at the door, beseeching
the victors to be merciful and to spare the lives of
the vanquished, when all and every thing in the
Mission would be freely placed at their disposal.

"What does the niggur say!" asked old Walker,
the leader of the mountaineers, of the interpreter.

"Well, he talks so queer, this hos can't rightly
make it out."

"Tell the old coon then to quit that, and make
them darned greasers clear out of the lodge, and
pock some corn and shucks here for the animals,
for they're nigh give out."

This being conveyed to him in mountain Spanish,
which fear alone made him understand, the padre
gave orders to the men to leave the Mission, advis-
ing them, moreover, not to recommence hostilities,
as himself was kept as hostage, and if a finger was
lifted against the mountaineers, he would be killed
at once, and the Mission burned to the ground.
Once inside, the hunters had no fear of attack,
they could have kept the building against all California; so, leaving a guard of two outside the gate,
and first seeing their worn-out animals supplied with
piles of corn and shucks, they made themselves at
home, and soon were paying attention to the hot
tortillas, meat, and chile colorado which were quickly placed before them, washing down the hot-spiced
viands with deep draughts of wine and brandy.   It

would have been amusing to have seen the faces of
these rough fellows as they gravely pledged each
other in the grateful liquor, and looked askance at
the piles of fruit served by the attendant Hebes.
These came in for no little share of attention, it
may be imagined; but the utmost respect was paid
to them, for your mountaineer, rough and bear-like
though he be, never, by word or deed, offends the
modesty of a woman, although sometimes obliged to
use a compulsory wooing, when time is not allowed
for regular courtship, and not unfrequently known
to jerk a New Mexican or Californian beauty behind his saddle, should the obdurate parents refuse
consent to their immediate union. It tickled the
Americans not a little to have all their wants supplied, and to be thus waited upon, by what they
considered the houris of paradise; and after their
long journey, and the many hardships and privations
they had suffered, their present luxurious situation
seemed scarcely real.

The hidalgo, released from the durance vile of
the lasso, assisted at the entertainment; his sense
of what was due to the "sangre regular" which
ran in his veins being appeased by the fact, that he
sat *above* the wild uncouth mountaineers, these preferring to squat crosslegged on the floor in their
own fashion, to the uncomfortable and novel luxury
of a chair. Killbuck, indeed, seemed to have quite
forgotten the use of such pieces of furniture. On
Fray Augustin offering him one, and begging him,

with many protestations, to be seated, that old
mountain worthy looked at it, and then at the
padre, turned it round, and at length comprehend-
ing the intention, essayed to sit. This he effected
at last, and sat grimly for some moments, when,
seizing the chair by the back, he hurled it out of
the open door, exclaiming,—" Wagh! this coon aint
hamshot anyhow, and don't want such fixins, he
don't;" and gathering his legs under his body,
reclined in the manner customary to him. There
was a prodigious quantity of liquor consumed that
night, the hunters making up for their many ban-
yans; but as it was the pure juice of the grape, it
had little or no effect upon their hard heads. They
had not much to fear from attacks on the part of
the Californians; but, to provide against all emergencies, the padre and the Gachupin were " hobbled," and confined in an inner room, to which there
was no ingress nor egress save through the door
which opened into the apartment where the mountaineers lay sleeping, two of the number keeping
watch. A fandango with the Indian girls had been
proposed by some of them, but Walker placed a
decided veto on this. He said " they had need of
sleep now, for there was no knowing what to-morrow might bring forth; that they had a long journey before them, and winter was coming on; they
would have to ' streak' it night and day, and sleep
when their journey was over, which would not be
until Pike's Peak was left behind them. It was now

October, and the way they'd have to hump it back
to the mountains would take the gristle off a painter's tail."

Young Ned Wooton was not to the fore when the
roll was called. He was courting the Sonora wench
Juanita, and to some purpose, for we may at once
observe, that the maiden accompanied the mountaineer to his distant home, and at the present moment is sharing his lodge on Hard-scrabble creek
of the upper Arkansa, having been duly and legally
married by Fray Augustin before their departure.

But now the snow on the ridge of the Sierra
Madre, and the nightly frosts; the angular flights
of geese and ducks constantly passing overhead;
the sober tints of the foliage, and the dead leaves
that strew the ground; the withering grass on the
plain, and the cold gusts, sometimes laden with
snow and sleet, that sweep from the distant snow-
clad mountains;—all these signs warn us to linger
no longer in the tempting valley of San Fernando,
but at once to pack our mules to cross the dreary
and desert plains and inhospitable sierras; and to
seek with our booty one of the sheltered bayous of
the Rocky Mountains.

On the third day after their arrival, behold our
mountaineers again upon the march, driving before
them—with the assistance of half-a-dozen Indians,
impressed for the first few days of the journey until
the cavallada get accustomed to travel without confusion—a band of four hundred head of mules and

horses, themselves mounted on the strongest and
fleetest they could select from at least a thousand.

Fray Augustin and the Hidalgo, from the house-
top, watched them depart: the former glad to get
rid of such unscrupulous guests at any cost, the
latter rather loath to part with his boon companions,
with whom he had quaffed many a quartillo of
Californian wine. Great was the grief, and violent
the sobbing, when all the girls in the Mission surrounded Juanita to bid her adieu; as she, seated *en
cavalier* on an easy pacing mule, bequeathed her
late companions to the keeping of every saint in the
calendar, and particularly to the great St Ferdinand himself, under whose especial tutelage all those
in the Mission were supposed to live. Pedrillo,
poor forsaken Pedrillo, a sullen sulky half-breed,
was overcome, not with grief, but with anger at the
slight put upon him, and vowed revenge. He of
the " sangre regular," having not a particle of
enmity in his heart, waved his arm—that arm with
which he had mowed down the enemies of Carlos
Quinto—and requested the mountaineers, if ever
fate should carry them to Spain, not to fail to visit
his quinta in the vega of Genil, which, with all in it,
he placed at their worships' disposal—con muchis-
sima franqueza.

Fat Fray Augustin likewise waved his arm, but
groaned in spirit as he beheld the noble band of
mules and horses, throwing back clouds of dust on
the plain where they had been bred. One noble

roan stallion seemed averse to leave his accustomed
pasture, and again and again broke away from the
band.　Luckily old Walker had taken the precaution to secure the " *bell-mare*" of the herd, and
mounted on her rode a-head, the animals all following their well-known leader.　As the roan galloped
back, the padre was in ecstasy.　It was a favourite
steed, and one he would have gladly ransomed at
any price.

" Ya viene, ya viene!" he cried out, " now, now
it's coming! hurra for the roan!" but, under the
rifle of a mountaineer, one of the Californians dashed
at it, a lasso whirling round his head, and turning
and twisting like a doubling hare, as the horse tried
to avoid him, at last threw the open coil over the
animal's head, and led him back in triumph to the
band.

" Maldito sea aquel Indio—curse that Indian!"
quoth the padre, and turned away.

And now our sturdy band—less two who had gone
under—were fairly on their way.　They passed the
body of their comrade who had been killed in the
fight before the Mission; the wolves, or Indian
dogs, had picked it to the bones; but a mound near
by, surrounded by a rude cross, showed where the
Californians (seven of whom were killed) had been
interred—thé pile of stones at the foot of the cross
testifying that many an *ave maria* had already
been said by the poor Indians, to save the souls of

their slaughtered companions from the pangs of purgatory.

For the first few days progress was slow and tedious. The confusion attendant upon driving so large a number of animals over a country without trail or track of any description, was sufficient to prevent speedy travelling; and the mountaineers, desirous of improving the pace, resolved to pursue a course more easterly, and to endeavour to strike the great SPANISH TRAIL, which is the route followed by the New Mexicans in their journeys to and from the towns of Puebla de los Angeles and Santa Fé. This road, however, crosses a long stretch of desert country, destitute alike of grass and water, save at a few points, the regular halting-places of the caravans; and as but little pasture is to be found at these places at any time, there was great reason to doubt, if the Santa Fé traders had passed this season, that there would not be sufficient grass to support the numerous cavallada, after the herbage had been laid under contribution by the traders' animals. However, a great saving of time would be effected by taking this trail, although it wound a considerable distance out of the way to avoid the impassable chain of the Sierra Nevada— the gap in those mountains through which the Americans had come being far to the southward, and at this late season probably obstructed by the snow.

Urged by threats and bribes, one of the Indians

agreed to guide the cavallada to the trail, which he declared was not more than five days' distant. As they advanced, the country became wilder and more sterile,—the valleys, through which several small streams coursed, alone being capable of supporting so large a number of animals. No time was lost in hunting for game; the poorest of the mules and horses were killed for provisions, and the diet was improved by a little venison when a deer casually presented itself near the camping ground. Of Indians they had seen not one; but they now approached the country of the Diggers, who infest the district through which the Spanish trail passes, laying contributions on the caravans of traders, and who have been, not inaptly, termed the "Arabs of the American desert." The Californian guide now earnestly entreated permission to retrace his steps, saying, that he should lose his life if he attempted to pass the Digger country alone on his return. He pointed to a snow-covered peak, at the foot of which the trail passed; and leave being accorded, he turned his horse's head towards the Mission of San Fernando.

Although the cavallada travelled, by this time, with much less confusion than at first, still, from the want of a track to follow, great trouble and exertion were required to keep the proper direction. The bell-mare led the van, carrying Walker, who was better acquainted with the country than the others; another hunter, of considerable distinction

in the band, on a large mule, rode by his side.
Then followed the cavallada, jumping and frisking
with each other, stopping whenever a blade of grass
showed, and constantly endeavouring to break away
to green patches which sometimes presented themselves in the plains. Behind the troop, urging them
on by dint of loud cries and objurgations, rode six
mountaineers, keeping as much as possible in a
line. Two others were on each flank to repress all
attempts to wander, and keep the herd in a compact
body. In this order the caravan had been crossing
a broken country, up and down ridges, all day, the
animals giving infinite trouble to their drivers, when
a loud shout from the advanced guard put them all
upon the *qui-vive*. Old Walker was seen to bran-
dish the rifle over his head and point before him,
and presently the cry of " The trail! the trail!"
gladdened all hearts with the anticipation of a
respite from the harassing labour of mule-driving.
Descending a broken ridge, they at once struck
into a distinct and tolerably well-worn track, into
which the cavallada turned as easily and instinc-
tively as if they had all their lives been accustomed
to travel on beaten roads. Along this they travelled
merrily—their delight being, however, alloyed by
frequent indications that hunger and thirst had
done their work on the mules and horses of the
caravans which had preceded them on the trail.
They happened to strike it in the centre of a long
stretch of desert, extending sixty miles without

either water or pasture; and many animals had perished here, leaving their bones to bleach upon the plain. The soil was sandy, but rocks and stones covered the surface, disabling the feet of many of the young horses and mules; several of which, at this early stage of the journey, were already abandoned. Traces of the wretched Diggers became very frequent; these abject creatures resorting to the sandy plains for the purpose of feeding upon the lizards which there abound. As yet they did not show; only at night they prowled around the camp, waiting a favourable opportunity to run the animals. In the present instance, however, many of the horses having been left on the road, the Diggers found so plentiful a supply of meat as to render unnecessary any attack upon the formidable mountaineers.

One evening the Americans had encamped, earlier than usual, on a creek well-timbered with willow and quaking-ash, and affording tolerable pasture; and although it was still rather early, they determined to stop here, and give the animals an opportunity to fill themselves. Several deer had jumped out of the bottom as they entered it; and La Bonté and Killbuck had sallied from the camp with their rifles, to hunt and endeavour to procure some venison for supper. Along the river banks, herds of deer were feeding in every direction, within shot of the belt of timber; and the two hunters had no difficulty in approaching and knocking over

two fine bucks within a few paces of the thicket.
They were engaged in butchering the animals,
when La Bonté, looking up from his work, saw
half-a-dozen Indians dodging among the trees,
within a few yards of himself and Killbuck. At
the same instant two arrows *thudded* into the carcass of the deer over which he knelt, passing but a
few inches from his head. Hollowing to his companion, La Bonté immediately seized the deer, and,
lifting it with main strength, held it as a shield
before him, but not before an arrow had struck
him in the shoulder. Rising from the ground he
retreated behind cover, yelling loudly to alarm
the camp, which was not five hundred yards' distant on the other side of the stream. Killbuck,
when apprised of the danger, ran bodily into the
plain, and, keeping out of shot of the timber, joined
La Bonté, who now, out of arrow-shot, threw down
his shield of venison and fired his rifle at the assailants. The Indians appeared at first afraid to leave
the cover; but three or four more joining them,
one a chief, they advanced into the plain, with
drawn bows, scattering wide apart, and running
swiftly towards the whites, in a zigzag course, in
order not to present a steady mark to their unerr-
ing rifles. The latter were too cautious to discharge
their pieces, but kept a steady front, with rifle at
shoulder. The Indians evidently disliked to approach nearer; but the chief, an old grizzled man,
incited them by word and gesture—running in

advance, and calling upon the others to follow
him.

"Ho, boy!" exclaimed Killbuck to his companion,
"that old coon must go under, or we'll get rubbed
out by these darned critturs."

La Bonté understood him. Squatting on the
ground, he planted his wiping-stick firmly at the
extent of his left arm, and resting the long barrel
of his rifle on his left hand, which was supported by
the stick, he took a steady aim and fired. The
Indian, throwing out his arms, staggered and let
fall his bow—tried hard to recover himself, and
then fell forward on his face. The others, seeing
the death of their chief, turned and made again for
the cover. "You darned critturs," roared Killbuck,
"take that!" and fired his rifle at the last one,
tumbling him over as dead as a stone. The camp
had also been alarmed. Five of them waded across
the creek and took the Indians in rear; their rifles
cracked within the timber, several more Indians
fell, and the rest quickly beat a retreat. The venison, however, was not forgotten; the two deer were
packed into camp, and did the duty of mule-meat
that night.

This lesson had a seasonable effect upon the Diggers, who made no attempt on the cavallada that
night or the next; for the camp remained two days
to recruit the animals.

We will not follow the party through all the dif-
ficulties and perils of the desert route, nor detail

Q

the various devilries of the Diggers, who constantly
sought opportunities to stampede the animals, or,
approaching them in the night as they grazed, fired
their arrows indiscriminately at the herd, trusting
that dead or disabled ones would be left behind,
and afford them a good supply of meat. In the
month of December the mountaineers crossed the
great dividing ridge of the Rocky Mountains, making their way through the snowy barrier with the
utmost difficulty, and losing many mules and horses
in the attempt. On passing the ridge, they at
once struck the head-springs of the Arkansa river,
and turned into the Bayou Salade. Here they
found a village of Arapahós, and were in no little
fear of leaving their cavallada with these dexterous
horse-thieves. Fortunately, the chief in command
was friendly to the whites, and restrained his young
men; and a present of three horses insured his
good offices. Still, the near neighbourhood of these
Indians being hardly desirable, after a few days'
halt, the Americans were again on their way, and
halted finally at the juncture of the Fontaine-qui-
bout with the Arkansa, where they determined to
construct a winter camp. They now considered
themselves at home, and at once set about building
a log-shanty capable of containing them all, and a
large corral for securing the animals at night, or in
case of Indian alarms. This they effected by felling several large cottonwoods, and throwing them
in the form of a hore-shoe : the entrance, however,

being narrower than in that figure, and secured by
upright logs, between which poles were fixed to be
withdrawn at pleasure. The house, or "fort"—as
any thing in the shape of a house is called in these
parts, where, indeed, every man must make his
house a castle—was loopholed on all sides, and
boasted a turf chimney of rather primitive construction; but which answered the purpose of drawing
the smoke from the interior. Game was plentiful
all around ;—bands of buffalo were constantly passing the Arkansa ; and there were always deer and
antelope within sight of the fort. The pasture,
too, was good and abundant—being the rich grama
or buffalo grass, which, although rather dry at this
season, still retains its fattening qualities; and the
animals soon began to improve wonderfully in condition and strength.

Of the four hundred head of mules and horses
with which they had started from California, but
one-half reached the Arkansa. Many had been
killed for food (indeed they had furnished the only
provisions during the journey), many had been
stolen by the Indians, or shot by them at night;
and many had strayed off and not been recovered.
We have omitted to mention that the Sonora girl,
Juanita, and her spouse, Ned Wooton, remained
behind at Roubideau's fort and rendezvous on the
Uintah, which our band had passed on the other
side of the mountains, whence they proceeded with
a party to Taos in New Mexico, and resided there

for some years, blessed with a fine family, &c. &c. &c., as the novels end.

As soon as the animals were fat and strong, they were taken down the Arkansa to Bent's Indian trading fort, about sixty miles below the mouth of Fontaine-qui-bout. Here a ready sale was found for them, mules being at that time in great demand on the frontier of the United States, and every season the Bents carried across the plains to Independence a considerable number collected in the Indian country, and in the upper settlements of New Mexico. While the mountaineers were descending the Arkansa, a little incident occurred, and some of the party very unexpectedly encountered an old friend. Killbuck and La Bonté, who were generally compañeros, were riding some distance ahead of the cavallada, passing at the time the mouth of the Huerfano or Orphan Creek, when, at a long distance before them, they saw the figure of a horseman, followed by two loose animals, descending the bluff into the timbered bottom of the river. Judging the stranger to be Indian, they spurred their horses and galloped in pursuit, but the figure ahead suddenly disappeared. However, they quickly followed the track, which was plain enough in the sandy bottom, that of a horse and two mules. Killbuck scrutinised the " sign," and puzzled over it a considerable time ; and at last exclaimed—" Wagh! this sign's as plain as mon beaver to me ; look at that hos-track, boy ; did ye ever see that afore ?"

" *Well*, I have!" answered La Bonté, peering down at it : " that ar shuffle-toe seems handy to me now, I *tell* you."

" The man as used to ride that hos is long gone under, but the hos, darn the old crittur, is old Bill Williams's, I'll swar by hook."

" Well, it aint nothin else," continued La Bonté, satisfying himself by a long look; " it's the old boy's hos as shure as shootin : and them Rapahos has rubbed him out at last, and raised his animals. Ho, boy ! let's lift their hair."

" Agreed," answered Killbuck; and away they started in pursuit, determined to avenge the death of their old comrade.

They followed the track through the bottom and into the stream, which it crossed, and, passing a few yards up the bank, entered the water again, when they could see nothing more of it. Puzzled at this, they sought on each side the river, but in vain; and, not wishing to lose more time in the search, they proceeded through the timber on the banks to find a good camping-place for the night, which had been their object in riding in advance of the cavallada. On the left bank, a short distance before them, was a heavy growth of timber, and the river ran in one place close to a high bluff, between which and the water was an almost impervious thicket of plum and cherry trees. The grove of timber ended before it reached this point, and but few scattered trees grew in the little glade which intervened, and

which was covered with tolerable grass. This being
fixed upon as an excellent camp, the two mountaineers rode into the glade, and dismounted close to the
plum and cherry thicket, which formed almost a
wall before them, and an excellent shelter from the
wind. Jumping off their horses, they were in the
act of removing the saddles from their backs, when
a shrill neigh burst from the thicket not two yards
behind them ; a rustling in the bushes followed, and
presently a man dressed in buck-skin, and rifle in
hand, burst out of the tangled brush, exclaiming in
an angry voice—

"Do'ee hy'ar now ?   I was nigh upon gut-shootin
some of e'e—I was now; thought e'e was darned
Rapahos, I did, and câched right off."

"Ho, Bill! what, old hos! not gone under yet ?"
cried both the hunters.   " Give us your paw."

"Do'ee now, if hy'ar ar'nt them boys as was
rubbed out on Lodge Pole (creek) a time ago.
Do'ee hyar ? if this aint 'some' now, I would'nt
say so."

Leaving old Bill Williams and our two friends to
exchange their rough but hearty greetings, we will
glance at that old worthy's history since the time
when we left him câching in the fire and smoke on
the Indian battle-ground in the Rocky Mountains.
He had escaped fire and smoke, or he would not
have been here on Arkansa with his old grizzled
Nez-percé steed.   On that occasion, the veteran
mountaineer had lost his two pack-animals and all

his beaver. He was not the man, however, to want a horse or mule as long as an Indian village was near at hand. Skulking, therefore, by day in cañons and deep gorges of the mountains, and travelling by night, he followed closely on the trail of the victorious savages, bided his time, struck his "coup," and recovered a pair of pack-horses, which was all he required. Ever since, he had been trapping alone in all parts of the mountains; had visited the rendezvous but twice for short periods, and then with full packs of beaver; and was now on his way to Bent's Fort, to dispose of his present loads of peltry, enjoy one good carouse on Taos whisky, and then return to some hole or corner in the mountains which he knew of, to follow in the spring his solitary avocation. He too had had his share of troubles, and had many Indian scrapes, but passed safely through all, and scarcely cared to talk of what he had done, so matter-of-fact to him were the most extraordinary of his perilous adventures.

Arrived at Bent's Fort, the party disposed of their cavallada, and then—respect for the pardonable weaknesses of our mountain friends prompts us to draw a veil over the furious orgies that ensued. A number of hunters and trappers were "in" from their hunting-grounds, and a village of Shians and some lodges of Kioways were camped round the fort. As long as the liquor lasted, and there was good store of alcohol as well as of Taos whisky, the Arkansa resounded with furious mirth—not unmixed

with graver scenes; for your mountaineer, ever
quarrelsome in his cups, is quick to give and take
offence, when rifles alone can settle the difference,
and much blood is spilt upon the prairie in his wild
and frequent quarrels.

Bent's Fort is situated on the left or northern
bank of the river Arkansa, about one hundred miles
from the foot of the Rocky Mountains—on a low
and level bluff of the prairie which here slopes
gradually to the water's-edge. The walls are built
entirely of adobes—or sun-burned bricks—in the
form of a hollow square, at two corners of which
are circular flanking towers of the same material.
The entrance is by a large gateway into the square,
round which are the rooms occupied by the traders
and employés of the host. These are small in size,
with walls coloured by a white-wash made of clay
found in the prairie. Their flat roofs are defended
along the exterior by parapets of adobe, to serve as
a cover to marksmen firing from the top; and along
the coping grow plants of cactus of all the varieties
common in the plains. In the centre of the square
is the press for packing the furs; and there are
three large rooms, one used as a store and magazine,
another as a council-room, where the Indians
assemble for their "talks," whilst the third is the
common dining-hall, where the traders, trappers,
and hunters, and all employés, feast upon the best
provender the game-covered country affords. Over
the culinary department presided of late years a

fair lady of colour, Charlotte by name, who was, as
she loved to say, " de onlee lady in de dam Injun
country," and who moreover was celebrated from
Long's Peak to the Cumbres Espanolás for slap-
jacks and pumpkin pies.

Here congregate at certain seasons the merchants
of the plains and mountains, with their stocks of
peltry. Chiefs of the Shian, the Kioway, and Arapahó, sit in solemn conclave with the head traders,
and smoke the "calumet" over their real and
imaginary grievances. Now O-cun-no-whurst, the
Yellow Wolf, grand chief of the Shian, complains
of certain grave offences against the dignity of his
nation! A trader from the " big lodge" (the fort)
has been in his village, and before the trade was
opened, in laying the customary chief's gift " on the
prairie"* has not " opened his hand," but " squeezed
out his present between his fingers," grudgingly,
and with too sparing measure. This was hard to
bear, but the Yellow Wolf would say no more!

Tah-kai-buhl, or, " he who jumps," is deputed
from the Kioway to warn the white traders not to
proceed to the Canadian to trade with the Comanche.
That nation is mad—a " heap mad" with the whites,
and has " dug up the hatchet" to " rub out" all
who enter its country. The Kioway loves the pale-
face, and gives him warning (and " he who jumps"

---

* Indian expression for a free gift.

looks as if he deserves something " on the prairie"
for his information).

Shawh-noh-qua-mish, " the peeled lodge-pole," is
there to excuse his Arapahó braves, who lately
made free with a band of horses belonging to the
fort. He promises the like shall never happen again,
and he, Shawh-noh-qua-mish, speaks with a " single
tongue." Over clouds of tobacco and kinnik-kinnik, these grave affairs are settled and terms arranged.

In the corral, groups of leather-clad mountaineers, with " decks" of " euker" and " seven up,"
gamble away their hard-earned peltries. The employés—mostly St Louis Frenchmen and Canadian
voyageurs—are pressing packs of buffalo skins,
beating robes, or engaged in other duties of a trading fort. Indian squaws, the wives of mountaineers,
strut about in all the pride of beads and fofarrow,
jingling with bells and bugles, and happy as paint
can make them. Hunters drop in with animals
packed with deer or buffalo meat to supply the
fort ; Indian dogs look anxiously in at the gateway, fearing to enter and encounter their natural enemies, the whites : and outside the fort, at
any hour of the day or night, one may safely wager
to see a dozen cayeutes or prairie wolves loping
round, or seated on their haunches, and looking
gravely on, waiting patiently for some chance offal
to be cast outside. Against the walls, groups of

Indians, too proud to enter without an invitation, lean, wrapped in their buffalo robes, sulky and evidently ill at ease to be so near the whites without a chance of fingering their scalp-locks; their white lodges shining in the sun, at a little distance from the river-banks; their horses feeding in the plain beyond.

The appearance of the fort is very striking, standing as it does hundreds of miles from any settlement, on the vast and lifeless prairie, surrounded by hordes of hostile Indians, and far out of reach of intercourse with civilised man; its mud-built walls inclosing a little garrison of a dozen hardy men, sufficient to hold in check the numerous tribes of savages ever thirsting for their blood. Yet the solitary stranger passing this lone fort, feels proudly secure when he comes within sight of the " stars and stripes" which float above the walls.

CHAPTER VIII.

AGAIN we must take a jump with La Bonté over a
space of several months; when we find him, in company of half a dozen trappers, amongst them his
inseparable compañero Killbuck, camped on the
Greenhorn creek, *en route* to the settlements of
New Mexico. They have a few mules packed with
beaver for the Taos market: but this expedition
has been planned more for pleasure than profit—a
journey to Taos valley being the only civilised
relaxation coveted by the mountaineers. Not a few
of the present band are bound thither with matrimonial intentions; the belles of Nuevo Mejico being
to them the *ne plus ultra* of female perfection, unit-
ing most conspicuous personal charms (although
coated with cosmetic *alegria*—an herb, with the
juice of which the women of Mexico hideously
bedaub their faces), with all the hard-working
industry of Indian squaws. The ladies, on their
part, do not hesitate to leave the paternal abodes,
and eternal tortilla-making, to share the perils and
privations of the American mountaineers in the distant wilderness. Utterly despising their own coun-
trymen, whom they are used to contrast with the

dashing white hunters who swagger in all the pride
of fringe and leather through their towns—they, as
is but natural, gladly accept husbands from the latter class; preferring the stranger, who possesses
the heart and strong right arm to defend them, to
the miserable cowardly "peládos," who hold what
little they have on sufferance of savage Indians, but
one degree superior to themselves.

Certainly no band of hunters that ever appeared
in the vale of Taos, numbered in its ranks a pro-
perer lot of lads than those now camped on Greenhorn, intent on matrimonial foray into the settlements of New Mexico.   There was young Dick
Wooton, who was "some" for his inches, being six
feet six, and as straight and strong as the barrel of
his long rifle.   Shoulder to shoulder with this "boy,"
stood Rube Herring, and not a hair's-breadth difference in height or size was there between them.
Killbuck, though mountain winters had sprinkled a
few snow-flakes on his head, *looked up* to neither;
and La Bonté held his own with any mountaineer
who ever set a trap in sight of Long's Peak or the
Snowy Range.   Marcellin—who, though a Mexican, despised his people and abjured his blood, having been all his life in the mountains with the white
hunters—looked down easily upon six feet and odd
inches.   In form a Hercules, he had the symmetry
of an Apollo; with strikingly handsome features,
and masses of long black hair hanging from his
slouching beaver over the shoulders of his buckskin

hunting shirt. He, as he was wont to say, was " no dam Spaniard, but ' mountainee man,' wagh!" Chabonard, a half-breed, was not lost in the crowd; —and, the last in height, but the first in every quality which constitutes excellence in a mountaineer, whether of indomitable courage, or perfect indifference to death or danger; with an iron frame capable of withstanding hunger, thirst, heat, cold, fatigue, and hardships of every kind; of wonderful presence of mind, and endless resources in times of peril; with the instinct of an animal, and the moral courage of a *man*—who was "taller" for his inches than KIT CARSON, paragon of mountaineers? *
Small in stature, and slenderly limbed, but with muscles of wire, with a fair complexion and quiet intelligent features, to look at Kit none would suppose that the mild-looking being before him was an incarnate devil in Indian fight, and had raised more hair from head of Redskins than any two men in the western country; and yet, thirty winters had scarcely planted a line or furrow on his clean-shaven face. No name, however, was better known in the mountains—from Yellow Stone to Spanish Peaks,

---

* Since the time of which we speak, Kit Carson has distinguished himself in guiding the several U. S. exploring expeditions, under Frémont, across the Rocky Mountains, and to all parts of Oregon and California; and for his services, the President of the United States presented the gallant Mountaineer with the commission of lieutenant in a newly raised regiment of mounted riflemen, of which his old leader Frémont is appointed colonel.

from Missouri to Columbia River—than that of Kit Carson, "raised" in Boonlick, county of Missouri State, and a credit to the diggins that gave him birth.

On Huerfano or Orphan Creek, so called from an isolated *hutte* which stands on a prairie near the stream, our party fell in with a village of Yuta Indians, at that time hostile to the whites. Both parties were preparing for battle, when Killbuck, who spoke the language, went forward with signs of peace, and after a talk with several chiefs, entered into an armistice, each party agreeing not to molest the other. After trading for a few deer-skins, which the Yutas are celebrated for dressing delicately fine, the trappers moved hastily on out of such dangerous company, and camped under the mountain on Oak Creek, where they forted in a strong position, and constructed a corral in which to secure their animals at night. At this point is a tolerable pass through the mountains, where a break occurs in a range, whence they gradually decrease in magnitude until they meet the sierras of Mexico, which connect the two mighty chains of the Andes and the Rocky Mountains. From the summit of the dividing ridge, to the eastward, a view is had of the vast sea of prairie which stretches away from the base of the mountains, in dreary barrenness, for nearly a thousand miles, until it meets the fertile valley of the great Missouri. Over this boundless expanse, nothing breaks the uninterrupted solitude of the view. Not a tree or atom of foliage relieves the eye; for the lines of scattered timber which belt the streams running from the mountains, are lost in the shadow of their stupendous height, and beyond this nothing is seen but the bare surface of the rolling prairie. In no other part of the chain are the grand characteristics of the Far West more strikingly displayed than from this pass. The mountains here rise, on the eastern side, abruptly from the plain, and the view over the great prairies is not therefore obstructed by intervening ridges. To the westward the eye sweeps over the broken spurs which stretch from the main range in every direction; whilst distant peaks, for the most part snow-covered, are seen at intervals rising isolated above the range. On all sides the scene is wild and dismal.

Crossing by this pass, the trappers followed the Yuta trail over a plain, skirting a pine-covered ridge, in which countless herds of antelope, tame as sheep, were pasturing. Numerous creeks intersect it, well timbered with oak, pine, and cedar, and well stocked with game of all kinds. On the eleventh day from leaving the Huerfano, they struck the Taos valley settlement on Arroyo Hondo, and pushed on at once to the village of Fernandez—sometimes, but improperly, called Taos. As the dashing band clattered through the village, the dark eyes of the reboso-wrapped muchachas peered from the doors of the adobe houses, each mouth armed with cigarito, which was at intervals removed to

allow utterance to the salutation to each hunter as
he trotted past of *Adios Americanos,*—" Welcome
to Fernandez!" and then they hurried off to prepare for the fandango, which invariably followed
the advent of the mountaineers. The men, however, seemed scarcely so well pleased; but leaned
sulkily against the walls, their sarapes turned
over the left shoulder, and concealing the lower
part of the face, the hand appearing from its upper
folds only to remove the eternal cigarro from their
lips. They, from under their broad-brimmed som-
breros, scowled with little affection upon the stalwart hunters, who clattered past them, scarcely
deigning to glance at the sullen Peládos, but paying
incomprehensible compliments to the buxom wenches
who smiled at them from the doors. Thus exchang-
ing salutations, they rode up to the house of an old
mountaineer, who had long been settled here with a
New Mexican wife, and who was the recognised
entertainer of the hunters when they visited Taos
valley, receiving in exchange such peltry as they
brought with them.

No sooner was it known that Los Americanos had
arrived, than nearly all the householders of Fernandez presented themselves to offer the use of their
" salas" for the fandango which invariably celebrated their arrival. This was always a profitable
event; for as the mountaineers were generally
pretty well " flush" of cash when on their " spree,"
and as open-handed as an Indian could wish, the

R

sale of whisky, with which they regaled all comers, produced a handsome return to the fortunate individual whose room was selected for the fandango. On this occasion the sala of the Alcalde Don Cornelio Vegil was selected and put in order; a general invitation was distributed; and all the dusky beauties of Fernandez were soon engaged in arraying themselves for the fête. Off came the coats of dirt and "alegnía" which had bedaubed their faces since the last "funcion," leaving their cheeks clear and clean. Water was profusely used, and their cuerpos were doubtless astonished by the unusual lavation. Their long black hair was washed and combed, plastered behind their ears, and plaited into a long queue, which hung down their backs. *Enaguas* of gaudy colour (red most affected) were donned, fastened round the waist with ornamented belts, and above this a snow-white *camisita* of fine linen was the only covering, allowing a prodigal display of their charms. Gold and silver ornaments, of antiquated pattern, decorate their ears and necks; and massive crosses of the precious metals, wrought from the gold or silver of their own placeres, hang pendant on their breasts. The enagua or petticoat, reaching about halfway between the knee and ancle, displays their well-turned limbs, destitute of stockings, and their tiny feet, thrust into quaint little shoes (*zapatitos*) of Cinderellan dimensions. Thus equipped, with the reboso drawn over their heads and faces, out of the folds of which their bril-

liant eyes flash like lightning, and each pretty
mouth armed with its cigarito, they coquettishly
enter the fandango.* Here, at one end of a long
room, are seated the musicians, their instruments
being generally a species of guitar, called heaca, a
bandolin, and an Indian drum, called *tombé*—one
of each. Round the room groups of New Mexicans
lounge, wrapped in the eternal sarape, and smoking
of course, scowling with jealous eyes at the more
favoured mountaineers. These, divested of their
hunting-coats of buckskins, appear in their bran-new
shirts of gaudy calico, and close fitting buckskin
pantaloons, with long fringes down the outside seam
from the hip to the ancle; with moccasins, ornamented with bright beads and porcupine quills.
Each, round his waist, wears his mountain-belt and
scalp-knife, ominous of the company he is in, and
some have pistols sticking in their belt.

The dances—save the mark!—are without form
or figure, at least those in which the white hunters
sport the "fantastic toe." Seizing his partner
round the waist with the gripe of a grisly bear, each
mountaineer whirls and twirls, jumps and stamps;
introduces Indian steps used in the "scalp" or
"buffalo" dances, whooping occasionally with unearthly cry, and then subsiding into the jerking step,
raising each foot alternately from the ground, so

* The word *fandango*, in New Mexico, is not applied to the
peculiar dance known in Spain by that name, but designates a
ball or dancing meeting.

much in vogue in Indian ballets. The hunters have
the floor all to themselves. The Mexicans have no
chance in such physical force dancing; and if a
dancing Peládo* steps into the ring, a lead-like
thump from a galloping mountaineer quickly sends
him sprawling, with the considerate remark—
"Quit, you darned Spaniard! you can't 'shine' in
this crowd."

During a lull, guagés† filled with whisky go the
rounds—offered to and seldom refused by the ladies
—sturdily quaffed by the mountaineers, and freely
swallowed by the Peládos, who drown their jealousy
and envious hate of their entertainers in potent
aguardiente. Now, as the guagés are oft refilled
and as often drained, and as night advances, so do
the spirits of the mountaineers become more boisterous, while their attentions to their partners
become warmer—the jealousy of the natives waxes
hotter thereat—and they begin to show symptoms
of resenting the endearments which the mountaineers bestow upon their wives and sweethearts. And
now, when the room is filled to crowding,—with two
hundred people, swearing, drinking, dancing, and
shouting—the half-dozen Americans monopolising
the fair, to the evident disadvantage of at least
threescore scowling Peládos, it happens that one of
these, maddened by whisky and the green-eyed

---

* A nickname for the idle fellows hanging about a Mexican
town, translated into "Greasers" by the Americans.

† Cask-shaped gourds.

monster, suddenly seizes a fair one from the waist-
encircling arm of a mountaineer, and pulls her from
her partner. Wagh!—La Bonté—it is he—stands
erect as a pillar for a moment, then raises his hand
to his mouth, and gives a ringing war-whoop—
jumps upon the rash Peládo, seizes him by the body
as if he were a child, lifts him over his head, and
dashes him with the force of a giant against the
wall.

The war, long threatened, has commenced;
twenty Mexicans draw their knives and rush upon
La Bonté, who stands his ground, and sweeps them
down with his ponderous fist, one after another, as
they throng around him. "Howgh-owgh-owgh-
owgh-h!" the well-known warhoop, bursts from the
throats of his companions, and on they rush to the
rescue. The women scream, and block the door in
their eagerness to escape; and thus the Mexicans
are compelled to stand their ground and fight.
Knives glitter in the light, and quick thrusts are
given and parried. In the centre of the room the
whites stand shoulder to shoulder—covering the
floor with Mexicans by their stalwart blows; but
the odds are fearful against them, and other assailants crowd up to supply the place of those who
fall.

The alarm being given by the shrieking women,
reinforcements of Peládos rushed to the scene of action, but could not enter the room, which was already
full. The odds began to tell against the moun-

taineers, when Kit Carson's quick eye caught sight
of a high stool or stone, supported by three long
heavy legs. In a moment he had cleared his way
to this, and in another the three legs were broken
off and in the hands of himself, Dick Wooton, and
La Bonté. Sweeping them round their heads, down
came the heavy weapons amongst the Mexicans with
wonderful effect—each blow, dealt by the nervous
arms of Wooton and La Bonté, mowing down a
good half-dozen of the assailants. At this the
mountaineers gave a hearty whoop, and charged the
wavering enemy with such resistless vigour, that
they gave way and bolted through the door, leaving
the floor strewed with wounded, many most dan-
gerously ; for, as may be imagined, a thrust from
the keen scalp-knife by the nervous arm of a mountaineer was no baby blow, and seldom failed to
strike home—up to the "Green River" * on the
blade.

The field being won, the whites, too, beat a quick
retreat to the house where they were domiciled, and
where they had left their rifles. Without their
trusty weapons they felt, indeed, unarmed ; and not
knowing how the affair just over would be followed
up, lost no time in making preparations for defence.
However, after great blustering on the part of the

---

* The knives used by the hunters and trappers are manufac-
tured at the " Green River " works, and have that name stamped
upon the blade.   Hence the mountain term for doing any thing
effectually is "up to Green River."

prefecto, who, accompanied by a *posse comitatus* of
" Greasers," proceeded to the house, and demanded
the surrender of all concerned in the affair—which
proposition was received with a yell of derision—
the business was compounded by the mountaineers
promising to give sundry dollars to the friends of
two of the Mexicans, who died during the night of
their wounds, and to pay for a certain amount of
masses to be sung for the repose of their souls in
purgatory. Thus the affair blew over; but for
several days the mountaineers never showed themselves in the streets of Fernandez without their rifles
on their shoulders, and refrained from attending
fandangos for the present, and until the excitement
had cooled down.

A bitter feeling, however, existed on the part of
the men; and one or two offers of a matrimonial
nature were rejected by the papas of certain ladies
who had been wooed by some of the white hunters,
and their hands formally demanded from the respective padres.

La Bonté had been rather smitten with the charms
of one Dolores Salazar—a buxom lass, more than
three parts Indian in her blood, but confessedly the
" beauty " of the Vale of Taos. She, by dint of eye,
and of nameless acts of elaborate coquetry, with which
the sex so universally bait their traps, whether in
the salons of Belgravia, or the rancherias of New
Mexico, contrived to make considerable havoc in
the heart of our mountaineer; and when once

Dolores saw she had made an impression, she followed up her advantage with all the arts the most
civilised of her sex could use when fishing for a
husband.

La Bonté, however, was too old a hunter to be
easily caught; and before committing himself, he
sought the advice of his tried companion Killbuck.
Taking him to a retired spot without the village, he
drew out his pipe and charged it—seated himself
cross-legged on the ground, and, with Indian gravity, composed himself for a " talk. "

" Ho, Killbuck ! " he began, touching the ground
with the bowl of his pipe, and then turning the stem
upwards for " *medicine* "—" Hyar's a child feels
squamptious like, and nigh upon ' gone beaver, '
he is—Wagh ! "

" Wagh ! " exclaimed Killbuck, all attention.

" Old hos, " continued the other, " thar's no use
câching anyhow what a niggur feels—so hyar's to
' put out. '   You're good for beaver *I* know; at
deer or buffler, or darned red Injun either, you're
' some.'   Now that's a fact.   ' Off-hand,' or ' with
a rest,' you make 'em ' come.'   You knows the
' sign ' of Injuns slick—Blackfoot or Sioux, Pawnee
or Burntwood, Zeton, Rapaho, Shian, or Shoshonée,
Yutah, Piyutah, or Yamhareek—their trail's as
plain as writin', old hos, to you. "

" Wagh ! " grunted Killbuck, blushing bronze at
all these compliments.

" Your sight ain't bad.   Elks is elk ; black-tail

deer ain't white-tails; and b'ar is b'ar to you, and
nothin' else, a long mile off and more."

" Wa-agh ! "

" Thar ain't a track as leaves its mark upon the
plains or mountains but you can read off-hand ; that
I've see'd myself. But tell me, old hos, can you
make understand the ' sign ' as shows itself in a
woman's breast ? "

Killbuck removed the pipe from his mouth, raised
his head, and puffed a rolling cloud of smoke into the
air,—knocked the ashes from the bowl, likewise
made his " medicine "—and answered thus :—

" From Red River, away up north amongst the
Britishers, to Heely (Gila) in the Spanish country—
from old Missoura to the Sea of Californy, I've trapped and hunted. I knows the Injuns and thar
' sign,' and they knows *me*, I'm thinkin. Thirty
winters has snowed on me in these hyar mountains,
and a niggur or a Spaniard * would larn ' some ' in
that time. This old tool " (tapping his rifle) " shoots
' center ' *she* does ; and if thar's game afoot, this
child knows ' bull ' from ' cow, ' and ought to could.
That deer is deer, and goats is goats, is plain as
paint to any but a greenhorn. Beaver's a cunning
crittur, but I've trapped a ' heap ; ' and at killing
meat when meat's a-running, I'll ' shine ' in the biggest kind of crowd. For twenty year I packed a
squaw along. Not one, but a man y. irst I had a

* Always alluding to Mexicans, who are invariably called
Spaniards by the Western Americans.

Blackfoot—the darndest slut as ever cried for fofarrow. I lodge-poled her on Colter's Creek, and made
her quit. My buffler hos, and as good as four packs
of beaver, I gave for old Bull-tail's daughter. He
was head chief of the Ricaree, and 'came' nicely
'round' me. Thar was'nt enough scarlet cloth, nor
beads, nor vermilion in Sublette's packs for her.
Traps wouldn't buy her all the fofarrow she wanted;
and in two years I'd sold her to Cross-Eagle for
one of Jake Hawkin's guns—this very one I hold
in my hands. Then I tried the Sioux, the Shian,
and a Digger from the other side, who made the
best moccasin as ever *I* wore. She was the best of
all, and was rubbed out by the Yutas in the Bayou
Salade. Bad was the best; and after she was gone
under I tried no more.

"Afore I left the settlements I know'd a white
gal, and she was some punkins. I have never seed
nothing as 'ould beat her. Red blood won't 'shine'
any ways you fix it; and though I'm h— for 'sign,'
a woman's breast is the hardest kind of rock to me,
and leaves no trail that I can see of. I've hearn
you talk of a gal in Memphis county; Mary Brand
you called her oncest. The gal I said *I* know'd, her
name I disremember, but she stands before me as
plain as Chimley Rock on Platte, and thirty year
and more har'nt changed a feature in her face, to
me.

"If you ask this child, he'll tell you to leave the
Spanish slut to her Greasers, and hold on till you

take the trail to old Missoura, whar white and Christian gals are to be had for axing. Wagh!"

La Bonté rose to his feet. The mention of Mary Brand's name decided him; and he said—

" Darn the Spaniard! she can't shine with me; come, old hos! let's move."

And, shouldering their rifles, the two campañeros returned to the Ronch. More than one of the mountaineers had fulfilled the object of their journey, and had taken to themselves a partner from amongst the belles of Taos, and now they were preparing for their return to the mountains. Dick Wooton was the only unfortuate one. He had wooed a damsel whose parents peremptorily forbade their daughter to wed the hunter, and he therefore made ready for his departure with considerable regret.

The day came, however. The band of mountaineers were already mounted, and those with wives in charge were some hours on the road, leaving the remainder quaffing many a stirrup-cup before they left. Dick Wooton was as melancholy as a buffalo bull in spring; and as he rode down the village, and approached the house of his lady-love, who stood wrapped in reboso, and cigarito in mouth, on the sill of the door, he turned away his head as if dreading to say adios. La Bonté rode beside him, and a thought struck him.

" Ho, Dick!" he said, " thar's the gal, and thar's the mountains: shoot sharp's the word."

Dick instantly understood him, and was "himself again." He rode up to the girl as if to bid her adieu, and she came to meet him. Whispering one word, she put her foot upon his, was instantly seized round the waist, and placed upon the horn of his saddle. He struck spurs into his horse, and in a minute was out of sight, his three companions covering his retreat, and menacing with their rifles the crowd which was soon drawn to the spot by the cries of the girl's parents, who had been astonished spectators of the daring rape.

The trapper and his bride, however, escaped scatheless, and the whole party effected a safe passage of the mountains, and reached the Arkansa, where the band was broken up,—some proceeding to Bent's Fort, and others to the Platte, amongst whom were Killbuck and La Bonté, still in company.

These two once more betook themselves to trapping, the Yellow Stone being their chief hunting-ground. But we must again leap over months and years, rather than conduct the reader through all their perilous wanderings, and at last bring him back to the camp on Bijou, where we first introduced him to our mountaineers; and as we have already followed them on the Arapaho trail, which they pursued to recover their stolen animals from a band of that nation, we will once again seat ourselves at the camp on Boiling Spring, where they had met a strange hunter on a solitary expedition to the Bayou Salade, whose double-barrelled rifle had excited their wonder and curiosity.

From him they learned also that a large band of Mormons were wintering on the Arkansa, *en route* to the Great Salt Lake and Upper California; and as our hunters had before fallen in with the advanced guard of these fanatic emigrants, and felt no little wonder that such helpless people should undertake so long a journey through the wilderness, the stranger narrated to them the history of the sect, which we shall shortly transcribe for the benefit of the reader.

CHAPTER IX.

THE Mormons were originally of the sect known as
" Latter-day Saints," which sect flourishes wherever
Anglo-Saxon gulls are found in sufficient numbers
to swallow the egregious nonsense of fanatic hum-
bugs who fatten upon their credulity. In the
United States they especially abounded; but, the
creed becoming "slow," one Joe Smith, a *smart*
man, arose from its ranks, and instilled a little life
into the decaying sect.

Joe, better known as the " Prophet Joe," was
taking his siesta one fine day, upon a hill in one of
the New England States, when an angel suddenly
appeared to him, and made known the locality of a
new Bible or Testament, which contained the history of the lost tribes of Israel; that these tribes
were no other than the Indian nations which possessed the continent of America at the time of its
discovery, and the remains of which still existed in
their savage state; that, through the agency of
Joe, these were to be reclaimed, collected into the
bosom of a church to be there established, according to principles which would be found in the won-

derful book—and which church was gradually to receive into its bosom all other churches, sects, and persuasions, with " unanimity of belief and perfect brotherhood."

After a certain probation, Joe was led in body and spirit to the mountain; by the angel who first appeared to him, was pointed out the position of the wonderful book, which was covered by a flat stone, on which would be found two round pebbles, called Urim and Thummim, and through the agency of which the mystic characters inscribed on the pages of the book were to be deciphered and translated. Joe found the spot indicated without any difficulty, cleared away the earth, and discovered hollow place formed by four flat stones; on removing the topmost one of which sundry plates of brass presented themselves, covered with quaint and antique carving; on the top lay Urim and Thummim (commonly known to the Mormons as Mummum and Thummum, the pebbles of wonderful virtue), through which the miracle of reading the plates of brass was to be performed.

Joe Smith, on whom the mantle of Moses had so suddenly fallen, carefully removed the plates and hid them, burying himself in woods and mountains whilst engaged in the work of translation. However, he made no secret of the important task imposed upon him, nor of the great work to which he had been called. Numbers at once believed him, but not a few were deaf to belief, and openly

derided him. Being persecuted (as the sect de-
clares, at the instigation of the authorities), and
many attempts being made to steal his precious
treasure, Joe, one fine night, packed his plates in a
sack of beans, bundled them into a Jersey waggon,
and made tracks for the West. Here he completed
the great work of translation, and not long after
gave to the world the " Book of Mormon," a work
as bulky as the Bible, and called " of Mormon," for
so was the prophet named by whose hand the history of the lost tribes had been handed down in the
plates of brass thus miraculously preserved for
thousands of years, and brought to light through
the agency of Joseph Smith.

The fame of the Book of Mormon spread over
all America, and even to Great Britain and Ireland.
Hundreds of proselytes flocked to Joe, to hear from
his lips the doctrine of Mormonism ; and in a very
brief period the Mormons became a numerous and
recognised sect, and Joe was at once, and by universal acclamation, installed as the head of the
Mormon church, and was ever after known by the
name of the " Prophet Joseph."

However, from certain peculiarities in their social
system, the Mormons became rather unpopular in
the settled States, and at length moved bodily into
Missouri, where they purchased several tracts of
land in the neighbourhood of Independence. Here
they erected a large building, which they called the
Lord's Store, where goods were collected on the

common account, and retailed to members of the
church at moderate prices. All this time their
numbers increased in a wonderful manner, and
immigrants from all parts of the States, as well as
Europe, continually joined them. As they became
stronger, they grew bolder and more arrogant in
their projects. They had hitherto been considered
as bad neighbours, on account of their pilfering
propensities, and their utter disregard of the con-
ventional decencies of society—exhibiting the greatest immorality, and endeavouring to establish
amongst their society an indiscriminate concubinage.
This was sufficient to produce an ill feeling against
them on the part of their neighbours, the honest
Missourians ; but they still tolerated their presence
amongst them, until the Saints openly proclaimed
their intention of seizing upon the country, and
expelling by force the present occupants—giving,
as their reason, that it had been revealed to their
prophets that the " Land of Zion" was to be possessed by themselves alone.

The sturdy Missourians began to think this was
a little too strong, and that, if they permitted such
aggressions any longer, they would be in a fair
way of being despoiled of their lands by the Mormon interlopers. At length matters came to a
crisis, and the Saints, emboldened by the impunity
with which they had hitherto carried out their
plans, issued a proclamation to the effect that all in
that part of the country, who did not belong to the

s

Mormon persuasion, must " clear out," and give up possession of their lands and houses. The Missourians collected in a body, burned the printing-press from which the proclamation had emanated, seized several of the Mormon leaders, and, after inflicting a summary chastisement, " tarred and feathered" them, and let them go.

To revenge this insult, the Mormons marshalled an army of Saints, and marched upon Independence, threatening vengeance against the town and people. Here they met, however, a band of sturdy backwoodsmen, armed with rifles, determined to defend the town against the fanatic mob, who, not relishing their appearance, refused the encounter, and surrendered their leaders at the first demand. The prisoners were afterwards released, on condition that the Mormons left that part of the country without delay.

Accordingly, they once more " took up their beds and walked," crossing the Missouri to Clay County, where they established themselves, and would finally have formed a thriving settlement but for their own acts of wilful dishonesty. At this time their blasphemous mummery knew no bounds. Joe Smith, and other prophets who had lately arisen, were declared to be chosen of God ; and it was the general creed that, on the day of judgment, the former would take his stand on the right hand of the judgment-seat, and that none would pass into the kingdom of heaven without his seal and touch.

One of their tenets was the faith in "spiritual matrimony." No woman, it appeared, would be admitted into heaven unless "passed" by a saint. To qualify them for this, it was necessary that the woman should first be received by the guaranteeing Mormon as an " earthly wife," in order that he did not pass in any of whom he had no knowledge. The consequence of this state of things may be imagined. The most debasing immorality was a precept of the order, and an almost universal concubinage existed amongst the sect, which at this time numbered at least forty thousand. Their disregard to the laws of decency and morality was such as could not be tolerated in any class of civilised society.

Again did the honest Missourians set their faces against this pernicious example, and when the county to which the Mormons had removed became more thickly settled, they rose to a man against the modern Gomorrah. The Mormons, by this time, having on their part gained considerable accession to their strength, thought to set the laws at defiance, organised and armed large bodies of men, in order to maintain the ascendency over the legitimate settlers, and bid fair to constitute an " imperium in imperio " in the State, and become the sole possessors of the public lands. This, of course, could not be tolerated. Governor Boggs at once ordered out a large force of State militia to put down this formidable demonstration, marched against the Mormons, and suppressed the insurrectionary movement without bloodshed.

From Clay County they moved still farther into the wilds, and settled at last in Caldwell County, where they built the town of "Far West," and here they remained for the space of three years.

During this time they were continually receiving converts to the faith, and many of the more ignorant country people were disposed to join them, being only deterred by the fear of incurring ridicule from the stronger-minded. The body of the Mormons seeing this, called upon their prophet, Joe Smith, to perform a miracle in public before all comers, which was to prove to those of their own people who still doubted the doctrine, the truth of what it advanced—(the power of performing miracles was stedfastly declared to be in their hands by the prophets)—and to enlist those who wavered in the Mormon cause.

The prophet instantly agreed, and declared that, upon a certain day, he would walk across the broad waters of the Missouri without wetting the soles of his feet. On the appointed day, the river banks were thronged by an expectant crowd. The Mormons sang hymns of praise in honour of their prophet, and were proud of the forthcoming miracle, which was to set finally at rest all doubt as to his power and sanctity.

This power of performing miracles and effecting

miraculous cures of the sick, was so generally believed by the Mormons, that physic was never used amongst them. The prophets visited the beds of the sick, and laid hands upon them, and if, as of course was almost invariably the case, the patient died, it was attributed to his or her want of faith; but if, on the contrary, the patient recovered, there was universal glorification on the miraculous cure.

Joe Smith was a tall, fine-looking man, of most plausible address, and possessed the gift of the gab in great perfection. At the time appointed for the performance of the walking-water miracle, he duly attended on the river banks, and descended barefoot to the edge of the water.

"My brethren!" he exclaimed in a loud voice, "this day is a happy one to me, to us all, who venerate the great and only faith. The truth of our great and blessed doctrine will now be proved before the thousands I see around me. You have asked me to prove by a miracle that the power of the prophets of old has been given to me. I say unto you, not only to me, but to all who have faith. I have faith, and can perform miracles—that faith empowers me to walk across the broad surface of that mighty river without wetting the soles of my unworthy feet; but if ye are to *see* this miracle performed, it is necessary that ye have faith also, not only in yourselves, but in me. Have ye this faith in yourselves?"

" We have, we have !" roared the crowd.

" Have ye the faith in me, that ye believe I can perform this miracle ?"

" We have, we have !" roared the crowd.

" Then," said Joe Smith, coolly walking away, " with such faith do ye know well that I *could,* but it boots not that I *should,* do it ; therefore, my brethren, doubt no more "—and Joe put on his boots and disappeared.

Being again compelled to emigrate, the Mormons proceeded into the state of Illinois, where, in a beautiful situation, they founded the new Jerusalem, which, it had been declared by the prophet Mormon, should rise out of the wilderness of the west, and where the chosen people should be collected under one church, and governed by the elders after a " spiritual fashion."

The city of Nauvoo soon became a large and imposing settlement. An enormous building, called the Temple of Zion, was erected, half church half hôtel, in which Joe Smith and the other prophets resided—and large storehouses were connected with it, in which the goods and chattels belonging to the community were kept for the common good.

However, here, as every where else, they were continually quarrelling with their neighbours ; and as their numbers increased, so did their audacity. A regular Mormon militia was again organised and armed, under the command of experienced officers, who had joined the sect ; and now the authority of the state government was openly defied. In consequence, the executive took measures to put down the nuisance, and a regular war commenced, and was carried on for some time, with no little bloodshed on both sides; and this armed movement is known in the United States as the Mormon war. The Mormons, however, who, it seemed, were much better skilled in the use of the tongue than the rifle, succumbed : the city of Nauvoo was taken, Joe Smith and other ringleading prophets captured ; and the former, in an attempt to escape from his place of confinement, was seized and shot. The Mormons declare he had long foretold his own fate, and that when the rifles of the firing party who were his executioners were levelled at the prophet's breast, a flash of lightning struck the weapons from their hands, and blinded for a time the eyes of the sacrilegious soldiers.

With the death of Joe Smith the prestige of the Mormon cause declined ; but still thousands of proselytes joined them annually, and at last the state took measures to remove them altogether, as a body, from the country.

Once again they fled, as they themselves term it, before the persecutions of the ungodly ! But this time their migration was far beyond the reach of their enemies, and their intention was to place between them the impassable barrier of the Rocky Mountains, and to seek a home and resting-place in the remote regions of the Far West.

This, the most extraordinary migration of modern times, commenced in the year 1845 ; but it was not till the following year that the great body of the Mormons turned their backs upon the settlements of the United States, and launched boldly out into the vast and barren prairies, without any fixed destination as a goal to their endless journey. For many months, long strings of Pittsburg and Conostaga waggons, with herds of horses and domestic cattle, wound their way towards the Indian frontier, with the intention of rendezvousing at Council Bluffs on the Upper Missouri. Here thousands of waggons were congregated, with their tens of thousands of men, women, and children, anxiously waiting the route from the elders of the church, who on their parts scarcely knew whither to direct the steps of the vast crowd they had set in motion. At length the indefinite destination of Oregon and California was proclaimed, and the long train of emigrants took up the line of march. It was believed the Indian tribes would immediately fraternise with the Mormons, on their approaching their country ; but the Pawnees quickly undeceived them by running off with their stock on every opportunity. Besides these losses, at every camp, horses, sheep, and oxen strayed away and were not recovered, and numbers died from fatigue and want of provender ; so that, before they had been many weeks on their journey, nearly all their cattle, which they had brought to stock their new country, were dead or missing, and those that were left were in most miserable condition.

They had started so late in the season, that the greater part were compelled to winter on the Platte, on Grand Island, and in the vicinity, where they endured the greatest privations and suffering from cold and hunger. Many who had lost their stock lived upon roots and pig-nuts; and scurvy, in a most malignant form, and other disorders, carried off numbers of the wretched fanatics.

Amongst them were many substantial farmers from all parts of the United States, who had given up their valuable farms, sold off all their property, and were dragging their irresponsible and unfortunate families into the wilderness—carried away by their blind and fanatic zeal in this absurd and incredible faith. There were also many poor wretches from different parts of England, mostly of the farm-labouring class, with wives and families, crawling along with helpless and almost idiotic despair, but urged forward by the fanatic leaders of the movement, who promised them a land flowing with milk and honey to reward them for all their hardships and privations.

Their numbers were soon reduced by want and disease. When too late, they often wished themselves back in the old country, and sighed many a time for the beer and bacon of former days, now preferable to the dry buffalo meat (but seldom obtainable) of the Far West.

Evil fortune pursued the Mormons, and dogged
their steps. The year following, some struggled
on towards the promised land, and of these a few
reached Oregon and California. Many were killed
by hostile Indians ; many perished of hunger, cold,
and thirst, in passing the great wilderness ; and
many returned to the States, penniless and crest-
fallen, and heartily cursing the moment in which
they had listened to the counsels of the Mormon
prophet. The numbers who reached their destination of Oregon, California, and the Great Salt
Lake, are computed at 20,000, of whom the United
States had an unregretted riddance.

One party had followed the troops of the American government intended for the conquest of New
Mexico and the Californias. Of these a battalion
was formed, and part of it proceeded to Upper
California ; but the way being impracticable for
waggons, some seventy families proceeded up the
Arkansa, and wintered near the mountains, intending to cross to the Platte the ensuing spring, and
join the main body of emigrants on their way by
the south pass of the Rocky Mountains.

In the wide and well-timbered bottom of the
Arkansa, the Mormons had erected a street of log
shanties, in which to pass the inclement winter.
These were built of rough logs of cottonwood, laid
one above the other, the interstices filled with mud,
and rendered impervious to wind or wet. At one
end of the row of shanties was built the " church "

or temple—a long building of huge logs, in which the prayer-meetings and holdings-forth took place. The band wintering on the Arkansa were a far better class than the generality of Mormons, and comprised many wealthy and respectable farmers from the western states, most of whom were accustomed to the life of woodmen, and were good hunters. Thus they were enabled to support their families upon the produce of their rifles, frequently sallying out to the nearest point of the mountains with a waggon, which they would bring back loaded with buffalo, deer, and elk meat, thereby saving the necessity of killing any of their stock of cattle, of which but few remained.

The mountain hunters found this camp a profitable market for their meat and deer-skins, with which the Mormons were now compelled to clothe themselves, and resorted there for that purpose—to say nothing of the attraction of the many really beautiful Missourian girls who sported their tall graceful figures at the frequent fandangoes. Dancing and preaching go hand in hand in Mormon doctrine, and the " temple " was generally cleared for a hop two or three times during the week, a couple of fiddles doing the duty of orchestra. A party of mountaineers came in one day, bringing some buffalo meat and dressed deer-skins, and were invited to be present at one of these festivals.

Arrived at the temple, they were rather taken aback by finding themselves in for a sermon, which

one of the elders delivered preparatory to the
"physical exercises." The preacher was one Brown
—called, by reason of his commanding a company
of Mormon volunteers, "Cap'en Brown"—a hard-
featured, black-coated man of five-and-forty, cor-
rectly got up in black continuations, and white
handkerchief round his neck, a costume seldom
seen at the foot of the Rocky Mountains. The
Cap'en, rising, cleared his voice, and thus commenced, first turning to an elder (with whom there
was a little rivalry in the way of preaching):—
"Brother Dowdle!"—(brother Dowdle blushed
and nodded : he was a long tallow-faced man, with
black hair combed over his face)—"I feel like
holding forth a little this afternoon, before we
glorify the Lord,—a—a—in the—a—holy dance.
As there are a many strange gentlemen now—
a—present, it's about right to tell 'em—a—
what our doctrine just is, and so I tells 'em right
off what the Mormons is. They are the chosen of
the Lord ; they are the children of glory, persecuted by the hand of man : they flies here to the
wilderness, and, amongst the *Injine* and the buffler,
they lifts up their heads, and cries with a loud
voice, Susannah, and hurray for the promised land !
Do you believe it ? I *know* it.

"They wants to know whar we're going. Whar
the church goes—thar we goes. Yes, to hell, and
pull the devil off his throne—that's what we'll do.
Do you believe it ? I *know* it.

" Thar's milk and honey in that land as we're goin' to, and the lost tribes of Israel is thar, and will jine us. They say as we'll starve on the road, bekase thar's no game and no water; but thar's manna up in heaven, and it 'll rain on us, and thar's prophets among us can make the water ' come.' Can't they, brother Dowdle ?"

" *Well*, they can."

" And now, what have the Gen*tiles* and the Phil-is*tines* to say against us Mormons? They says we're thieves, and steal hogs; yes, d—— 'em! they say we has as many wives as we like. So we have. I've twenty—forty, myself, and mean to have as many more as I can get. But it's to pass unfortunate females into heaven that I has 'em— yes, to prevent 'em going to roaring flames and damnation that I does it.

" Brother Dowdle," he continued, in a hoarse, low voice, " I've ' give out,' and think we'd better begin the exercises grettful to the Lord."

Brother Dowdle rose, and, after saying that " he didn't feel like saying much, begged to remind all hands, that dancing was solemn like, to be done with proper devotion, and not with laughing and talking, of which he hoped to hear little or none; that joy was to be in their hearts, and not on their lips; that they danced for the glory of the Lord, and not their own amusement, as did the Gen*tiles*." After saying thus, he called upon brother Ezra to " strike up :" sundry couples stood forth, and the ball commenced.

Ezra of the violin was a tall, shambling Missourian, with a pair of " homespun " pantaloons thrust into the legs of his heavy boots. Nodding his head in time with the music, he occasionally gave instructions to such of the dancers as were at fault, singing them to the tune he was playing, in a dismal nasal tone,—

> " Down the centre—hands across,"
> " You, Jake Herring—thump it,"
> " Now, you all go right a-head—
> Every one of you hump it.
> Every one of you—*hump it.*"

The last words being the signal that all should clap the steam on, which they did *con amore*, and with comical seriousness.

A mountaineer, Rube Herring, whom we have more than once met in the course of this narrative, became a convert to the Mormon creed, and held forth its wonderful doctrines to such of the incredulous trappers as he could induce to listen to him. Old Rube stood nearly six feet six in height, and was spare and bony in make. He had picked up a most extraordinary cloth coat amongst the Mormons, which had belonged to some one his equal in stature. This coat, which was of a snuff-brown colour, had its waist about a hand's span from the nape of Rube's neck, or about a yard above its

proper position, and the skirts reached to his
ancles. A slouching felt-hat covered his head, from
which long black hair escaped, hanging in flakes
over his lantern-jaws. His pantaloons of buckskin
were shrunk with wet, and reached midway between his knees and ancles, and his huge feet were
encased in moccasins of buffalo-cow skin.

Rube was never without the book of Mormon in
his hand, and his sonorous voice might be heard, at
all hours of the day and night, reading passages
from its wonderful pages. He stood the badgering
of the hunters with most perfect good humour, and
said there never was such a book as that ever
before printed; that the Mormons were the " biggest kind " of prophets, and theirs the best faith
ever man believed in.

Rube had let out one day that he was to be hired
as guide by this party of Mormons to the Great
Salt Lake; but their destination being changed,
and his services not required, a wonderful change
came over his mind. He was, as usual, book of
Mormon in hand, when brother Brown announced
the change in their plans; at which the book was
cast into the Arkansa, and Rube exclaimed—" Cuss
your darned Mummum and Thummum! thar's not
one among you knows ' fat cow ' from ' poor bull,'
and you may go h—— for me." And turning
away, old Rube spat out a quid of tobacco and his
Mormonism together.

Amongst the Mormons was an old man, named Brand, from Memphis county, state of Tennessee, with a family of a daughter and two sons, the latter with their wives and children. Brand was a wiry old fellow, nearly seventy years of age, but still stout and strong, and wielded axe or rifle better than many a younger man. If truth be told, he was not a very red-hot Mormon, and had joined them as much for the sake of company to California, whither he had long resolved to emigrate, as from any implicit credence in the faith. His sons were strapping fellows, of the sterling stuff that the Western pioneers are made of; his daughter Mary, a fine woman of thirty, for whose state of single blessedness there must doubtless have been sufficient reason; for she was not only remarkably handsome, but was well known in Memphis to be the best-tempered and most industrious young woman in those diggings. She was known to have received several advantageous offers, all of which she had refused; and report said, that it was from having been disappointed in very early life in an *affaire du cœur*, at an age when such wounds sometimes strike strong and deep, leaving a scar difficult to heal. Neither his daughter, nor any of his family, had been converted to the Mormon doctrine, but had ever kept themselves aloof, and refused to join or associate with them; and, for this reason, the family had been very unpopular with the Mormon families on the Arkansa; and hence, probably,

one great reason why they now started alone on
their journey.

Spring had arrived, and it was time the Mormons should proceed on their march ; but whether already tired of the sample they had had
of life in the wilderness, or fearful of encountering
the perils of the Indian country, not one amongst
them, with the exception of old Brand, seemed
inclined to pursue the journey farther. That old
backwoodsman, however, was not to be deterred,
but declared his intention of setting out alone, with
his family, and risking all the dangers to be anticipated.

One fine sunny evening in April of 1847, when
the cottonwoods on the banks of the Arkansa began
to put forth their buds, and robins and blue-birds
—harbingers of spring—were hopping, with gaudy
plumage, through the thickets, three white-tilted
Conostoga waggons emerged from the timbered
bottom of the river, and rumbled slowly over the
prairie, in the direction of the Platte's waters.
Each waggon was drawn by eight oxen, and contained a portion of the farming implements and
household utensils of the Brand family. The teams
were driven by the young boys, the men following
in rear with shouldered rifles—Old Brand himself
mounted on an Indian horse, leading the advance.
The women were safely housed under the shelter of
the waggon tilts, and out of the first the mild face
of Mary Brand smiled adieu to many of her old

T

companions who had accompanied them thus far, and now wished them "God-speed" on their long journey. Some mountaineers, too, galloped up, dressed in buckskin, and gave them rough greeting—warning the men to keep their "eyes skinned," and look out for the Arapahos, who were out on the waters of the Platte. Presently all retired, and then the huge waggons and the little company were rolling on their solitary way through the deserted prairies—passing the first of the many thousand miles which lay between them and the "setting sun," as the Indians style the distant regions of the Far West. And on, without casting a look behind him, doggedly and boldly marched old Brand, followed by his sturdy family.

They made but a few miles that evening, for the first day the *start* is all that is effected; and nearly the whole morning is taken up in getting fairly under weigh. The loose stock had been sent off earlier, for they had been collected and corralled the previous night; and, after a twelve hours' fast, it was necessary they should reach the end of the day's journey betimes. They found the herd grazing in the bottom of the Arkansa, at a point previously fixed upon for their first camp. Here the oxen were unyoked, and the waggons drawn up so as to form the three sides of a small square. The women then descended from their seats, and prepared the evening meal. A huge fire was kindled before the waggons, and round this the whole party collected;

whilst large kettles of coffee boiled on it, and hoe-cakes baked upon the embers.

The women were sadly downhearted, as well they might be, with the dreary prospect before them; and poor Mary, when she saw the Mormon encampment shut out from her sight by the rolling bluffs, and nothing before her but the bleak, barren prairie, could not divest herself of the idea that she had looked for the last time on civilised fellow-creatures, and fairly burst into tears.

In the morning the heavy waggons rolled on again across the upland prairies, to strike the trail used by the traders in passing from the south fork of the Platte to the Arkansa. They had for guide a Canadian voyageur, who had been in the service of the Indian traders, and knew the route well, and who had agreed to pilot them to Fort Lancaster, on the north fork of the Platte. Their course led for about thirty miles up the Boiling Spring River, whence they pursued a north-easterly course to the dividing ridge which separates the waters of the Platte and Arkansa. Their progress was slow, for the ground was saturated with wet, and exceedingly heavy for the cattle, and they scarcely advanced more than ten miles a-day.

At the camp-fire at night, Antoine, the Canadian guide, amused them with tales of the wild life and perilous adventures of the hunters and trappers who make the mountains their home; often extorting a scream from the women by the description of some scene of Indian fight and slaughter, or beguiling them of a commiserating tear by the narrative of the sufferings and privations endured by those hardy hunters in their arduous life.

Mary listened with the greater interest, since she remembered that such was the life which had been led by one very dear to her—by one, long supposed to be dead, of whom she had never but once, since his departure, nearly fifteen years before, heard a syllable. Her imagination pictured him as the bravest and most daring of these adventurous hunters, and conjured up his figure charging through the midst of whooping savages, or stretched on the ground perishing from wounds, or cold, or famine.

Amongst the characters who figured in Antoine's stories, a hunter named La Bonté was made conspicuous for deeds of hardiness and daring. The first mention of the name caused the blood to rush to Mary's face : not that she for a moment imagined it was her La Bonté, for she knew the name was a common one; but, associated with feelings which she had never got the better of, it recalled a sad epoch in her former life, to which she could not look back without mingled pain and pleasure.

Once only, and about two years after his departure, had she ever received tidings of her former lover. A mountaineer had returned from the Far West to settle in his native State, and had found his way to the neighbourhood of old Brand's farm.

Meeting him by accident, Mary, hearing him speak of the mountain hunters, had inquired, tremblingly, after La Bonté. Her informant knew him well—had trapped in company with him—and had heard at the trading fort, whence he had taken his departure for the settlements, that La Bonté had been killed on the Yellow Stone by Blackfeet; which report was confirmed by some Indians of that nation. This was all she had ever learned of the lover of her youth.

Now, upon hearing the name of La Bonté so often mentioned by Antoine, a vague hope was raised in her breast that he was still alive, and she took an opportunity of questioning the Canadian closely on the subject.

" Who was this La Bonté, Antoine, who you say was so brave a mountaineer?" she asked one day.

" J'ne sais pas; he vas un beau garçon, and strong comme le diable—enfant de garce, mais he pas not care a dam for les sauvages, pe gar. He shoot de centare avec his carabine; and ride de cheval comme one Comanche. He trap heap castor, (what you call beevare,) and get plenty dollare—mais he open hand vare wide—and got none too. Den, he hont vid de Blackfoot and avec de Cheyenne, and all round de montaignes he hont dam sight."

" But, Antoine, what became of him at last? and why did he not come home, when he made so many dollars?" asked poor Mary.

"Enfant de garce, mais pourquoi he com home? Pe gar, de montaigne-man, he love de montaigne and de prairie more better dan he love de grandes villes—même de Saint Louis ou de Montreal. Wagh! La Bonté, well, he one montaigne-man, wagh! He love de buffaloe and de chevreaux plus que de bœuf and de mouton, may be. Mais on-dit dat he have autre raison—dat de gal he lofe in Missouri not lofe him, and for dis he not go back. Mais now he go ondare, m' on dit. He vas go to de Californe, may be to steal de hos and de mule —pe gar, and de Espagnols rub him out, and take his hair, so he mort."

"But are you sure of this?" she asked, trembling with grief.

"Ah, now, j'ne suis pas sûr, mais I tink you know dis La Bonté. Enfant de garce, maybe you de gal in Missouri he lofe, and not lofe him. Pe gar! 'fant de garce! fort beau garçon dis La Bonté, pourquoi you ne l'aimez pas? Maybe he not gone ondare. Maybe he turn op, autrefois. De trappares, dey go ondare tree, four, ten times, mais dey turn op twenty time. De sauvage not able for kill La Bonté, ni de dam Espagnols. Ah, non! ne craignez pas; pe gar, he not gone ondare encore."

Spite of the good-natured attempts of the Canadian, poor Mary burst into a flood of tears: not that the information took her unawares, for she long had believed him dead; but because the very mention of his name awoke the strongest feelings

within her breast, and taught her how deep was
the affection she had felt for him whose loss and
violent fate she now bewailed.

As the waggons of the lone caravan roll on towards the Platte, we return to the camp where La
Bonté, Killbuck, and the stranger, were sitting
before the fire when last we saw them :—Killbuck
loquitur :—

" The doins of them Mormon fools can't be beat
by Spaniards, stranger.   Their mummums and
thummums you speak of won't ' shine' whar Injuns
are about ; nor pint out a trail, whar nothin crossed
but rattler-snakes since fust it snow'd on old Pike's
Peak.   If they pack along them *profits*, as you tell
of, who can make it rain hump-ribs and marrow-
guts when the crowd gets out of the buffler range,
they are ' some,' now, that's a fact.   But this child
don't believe it.   I'd laugh to get a sight on these
darned Mormonites, I would.   They're ' no account,'
I guess ; and it's the ' meanest' kind of action to
haul their women critters and their young 'uns to
sech a starving country as the Californys."

" They are not all Mormons in the crowd," said
the strange hunter ; " and there's one family
amongst them with some smartish boys and girls, I
tell you.   Their name 's Brand."

La Bonté looked up from the lock of his rifle,
which he was cleaning—but either didn't hear, or,
hearing, didn't heed, for he continued his work.

" And they are going to part company," con-

tinued the stranger, " and put out alone for Platte
and the South Pass."

" They'll lose their hair, I'm thinking," said Killbuck, " if the Rapahos are out thar."

" I hope not," continued the other, " for there's
a girl amongst them worth more than that."

" Poor beaver!" said La Bonté, looking up from
his work. " I'd hate to see any white gal in the
hands of Injuns, and of Rapahos worse than all.
Where does she come from, stranger?"

" Down below St Louis, from Tennessee, I've
heard them say."

" Tennessee," cried La Bonté,—" hurrah for the
old State! What's her name, stran——" At this
moment Killbuck's old mule pricked her ears and
snuffed the air, which action catching La Bonté's
eye, he rose abruptly, without waiting a reply to
his question, and exclaimed, " The old mule smells
Injuns, or I'm a Spaniard!"

The hunter did the old mule justice, and she well
maintained her reputation as the best " guard" in
the mountains; for in two minutes an Indian stalked
into the camp, dressed in a cloth capote, and in odds
and ends of civilised attire.

" Rapaho," cried Killbuck, as soon as he saw
him; and the Indian catching the word, struck his
hand upon his breast, and exclaimed, in broken
Spanish and English mixed, " Si, si, me Arapaho,
white man amigo. Come to camp—eat heap *carne*
—me amigo white man. Come from Pueblo—hunt

cibola—me gun break—*no puedo matar nada:
mucha hambre* (very hungry),—heap eat."

Killbuck offered his pipe to the Indian, and spoke
to him in his own language, which both he and La
Bonté well understood. They learned that he was
married to a Mexican woman, and lived with some
hunters at the Pueblo fort on the Arkansa. He volunteered the information that a war party of his people
were out on the Platte trail to intercept the Indian
traders on their return from the North Fork; and
as some " Mormones" had just started with three
waggons in that direction, he said his people would
make a " roise." Being muy amigo himself to the
whites, he cautioned his present companions from
crossing to the " divide," as the " braves," he said,
were a " heap" mad, and their hearts were " big,"
and nothing in the shape of white skin would live
before them.

" Wagh!" exclaimed Killbuck, " the Rapahos
know me, I'm thinking; and small gain they've
made against this child. I've knowed the time
when my gun-cover couldn't hold more of their
scalps."

The Indian was provided with some powder, of
which he stood in need; and, after gorging as much
meat as his capacious stomach would hold, he left
the camp; and started into the mountain.

The next day our hunters started on their journey down the river, travelling leisurely, and stopping wherever good grass presented itself. One

morning they suddenly struck a wheel trail, which
left the creek banks and pursued a course at right
angles to it, in the direction of the " divide." Killbuck pronounced it but a few hours old, and that
of three waggons drawn by oxen.

" Wagh!" he exclaimed, " if them poor devils of
Mormonites ain't going head first into the Rapaho
trap. They'll be ' gone beaver' afore long."

" Ay," said the strange hunter, " these are the
waggons belonging to old Brand, and he has started
alone for Laramie. I hope nothing will happen to
them."

" Brand!" muttered La Bonté. " I knowed that
name mighty well once, years agone; and should
hate the worst kind that mischief happened to any
one who bore it. This trail's as fresh as paint; and
it goes against me to let these simple critters help
the Rapahos to their own hair. This child feels
like helping 'em out of the scrape. What do you
say, old hos?"

" I thinks with you, boy," answered Killbuck,
" and go in for following this waggon trail, and telling the poor critters that thar's danger ahead of
them. What's your talk, stranger?"

" I go with you," shortly answered the latter;
and both followed quickly after La Bonté, who was
already trotting smartly on the trail.

Meanwhile the three waggons, containing the
household gods of the Brand family, rumbled slowly
over the rolling prairie, and towards the upland

ridge of the " divide," which, studded with dwarf
pine and cedar thicket, rose gradually before them.
They travelled with considerable caution, for already
the quick eye of Antoine had discovered recent
Indian sign upon the trail, and, with mountain
quickness, had at once made it out to be that of a
war party; for there were no horses with them,
and, after one or two of the moccasin tracks, the
mark of a rope which trailed upon the ground was
sufficient to show him that the Indians were provided with the usual lasso of skin, with which to
secure the horses stolen in the expedition. The men
of the party were consequently all mounted and
thoroughly armed, the waggons moved in a line
abreast, and a sharp look-out was kept on all sides.
The women and children were all consigned to the
interior of the waggons; and the latter had also
guns in readiness, to take their part in the defence,
should an attack be made.

However, they had seen no Indians, and no fresh
sign, for two days after they left the Boiling Spring
River, and they began to think they were well out
of their neighbourhood. One evening they camped
on a creek called Black Horse, and, as usual, had
corralled the waggons, and forted as well as cir-
cumstances would permit, when three or four Indians
suddenly appeared on a bluff at a little distance,
and, making signals of peaceable intentions, approached the camp. Most of the men were absent
at the time, attending to the cattle or collecting

fuel, and only old Brand and one of his young grandchildren, about fourteen years old, remained in camp. The Indians were hospitably received, and regaled with a smoke, after which they began to evince their curiosity by examining every article lying about, and signifying their wishes that it should be given to them. Finding their hints were not taken, they laid hold of several things which took their fancies, and, amongst others, of the pot which was boiling on the fire, and with which one of them was about very coolly to walk off, when old Brand, who up to this moment had retained possession of his temper, seized it out of the Indian's hand, and knocked him down. One of the others instantly began to draw the buckskin cover from his gun, and would no doubt have taken summary vengeance for the insult offered to his companion, when Mary Brand courageously stepped up to him, and, placing her left hand upon the gun which he was in the act of uncovering, with the other pointed a pistol at his breast.

Whether daunted by the bold act of the girl, or admiring her devotion to her father, the Indian drew himself back, exclaimed " Howgh!" and drew the cover again on his piece, went up to old Brand, who all this time looked him sternly in the face, and, shaking him by the hand, motioned at the same time to the others to be peaceable.

The other whites presently coming into camp, the Indians sat quietly down by the fire, and, when the supper was ready, joined in the repast, after which they gathered their buffalo robes about them, and quietly withdrew. Meanwhile Antoine, knowing the treacherous character of the savages, advised that the greatest precaution should be taken to secure the stock ; and before dark, therefore, all the mules and horses were hobbled and secured within the corral, the oxen being allowed to feed at liberty —for the Indians scarcely care to trouble themselves with such cattle. A guard was also set round the camp, and relieved every two hours ; the fire was extinguished, lest the savages should aim, by its light, at any of the party, and all slept with rifles ready at their sides. However, the night passed quietly, and nothing disturbed the tranquillity of the camp. The prairie wolves loped hungrily around, and their mournful cry was borne upon the wind as they chased deer and antelope on the neighbouring plain ; but not a sign of lurking Indians was seen or heard.

In the morning, shortly after sunrise, they were in the act of yoking the oxen to the waggons, and driving in the loose animals which had been turned out to feed at daybreak, when some Indians again appeared upon the bluff, and, descending it, confidently aproached the camp. Antoine strongly advised their not being allowed to enter ; but Brand, ignorant of Indian treachery, replied that, so long as they came as friends, they could not be deemed enemies, and allowed no obstruction to be offered to their approach. It was now observed that they were all painted, armed with bows and arrows, and divested of their buffalo robes, appearing naked to the breech-clout, their legs only being protected by deerskin leggings, reaching to the middle of the thigh. Six or seven first arrived, and others quickly followed, dropping in one after the other, until a score or more were collected round the waggons. Their demeanour, at first friendly, soon changed as their numbers increased, and they now became urgent in their demands for powder and lead, and bullying in their manner. A chief accosted Brand, and, through Antoine, informed him "that, unless the demands of his braves were acceded to, he could not be responsible for the consequences; that they were out on the 'war-trail,' and their eyes were red with blood, so that they could not distinguish between white and Yuta scalps; that the party, with all their women and waggons, were in the power of the Indian 'braves,' and therefore the white chief's best plan was to make the best terms he could; that all they required was that they should give up their guns and ammunition 'on the prairie,' and all their mules and horses—retaining the 'medicine' buffaloes (the oxen) to draw their waggons."

By this time the oxen were yoked, and the teamsters, whip in hand, only waited the word to start. Old Brand foamed whilst the Indian stated his demands, but, hearing him to the end, exclaimed, "Darn the red devil! I wouldn't give him a

grain of powder to save my life. Put out, boys!"
—and, turning to his horse, which stood ready sad-
dled, was about to mount, when the Indians sprang
at once upon the waggons, and commenced their
attack, yelling like fiends.

One jumped upon old Brand, pulled him back as
he was rising in the stirrup, and drew his bow upon
him at the same moment. In an instant the old
backwoodsman pulled a pistol from his belt, and,
putting the muzzle to the Indian's heart, shot him
dead. Another Indian, flourishing his war-club,
laid the old man at his feet; whilst some dragged
the women from the waggons, and others rushed
upon the men, who made brave fight in their defence.

Mary, when she saw her father struck to the
ground, sprang with a shrill cry to his assistance;
for at that moment a savage, frightful as red paint
could make him, was standing over his prostrate
body, brandishing a glittering knife in the air, preparatory to thrusting it into the old man's breast.
For the rest, all was confusion : in vain the small
party of whites struggled against overpowering
numbers. Their rifles cracked but once, and they
were quickly disarmed; whilst the shrieks of the
women and children, and the loud yells of the
Indians, added to the scene of horror and confusion.
As Mary flew to her father's side, an Indian threw
his lasso at her, the noose falling over her shoulders,
and, jerking it tight, he uttered a delighted yell as

the poor girl was thrown back violently to the ground. As she fell, another deliberately shot an arrow at her body, whilst the one who had thrown the lasso rushed forward, his scalp-knife flashing in his hand, to seize the bloody trophy of his savage deed. The girl rose to her knees, and looked wildly towards the spot where her father lay bathed in blood; but the Indian pulled the rope violently, dragged her some yards upon the ground, and then rushed with a yell of vengeance upon his victim. He paused, however, as at that moment a shout as fierce as his own sounded at his very ear; and, looking up, he saw La Bonté gallopping madly down the bluff, his long hair and the fringes of his hunting-shirt and leggins flying in the wind, his right arm supporting his trusty rifle, whilst close behind him came Killbuck and the stranger. Dashing with loud hurrahs to the scene of action, La Bonté, as he charged down the bluff, caught sight of the girl struggling in the hands of the ferocious Indian. Loud was the war-shout of the mountaineer, as he struck his heavy spurs to the rowels in his horse's side, and bounded like lightning to the rescue. In a single stride he was upon the Indian, and, thrusting the muzzle of his rifle into his very breast, he pulled the trigger, driving the savage backward by the blow itself, at the same moment that the bullet passed through his heart, and tumbled him over stone-dead. Throwing down his rifle, La Bonté wheeled his obedient horse, and, drawing a pistol from his belt, again charged the enemy, among whom Killbuck and the stranger were dealing death-giving blows. Yelling for victory, the mountaineers rushed at the Indians; and they, panic-struck at the sudden attack, and thinking this was but the advanced guard of a large band, fairly turned and fled, leaving five of their number dead upon the field.

Mary, shutting her eyes to the expected death-stroke, heard the loud shout La Bonté gave in charging down the bluff, and, again looking up, saw the wild-looking mountaineer rush to her rescue, and save her from the savage by his timely blow. Her arms were still pinned by the lasso, which prevented her from rising to her feet; and La Bonté was the first to run to aid her, as soon as the fight was fairly over. He jumped from his horse, cut the skin rope which bound her, raised her from the ground, and, upon her turning up her face to thank him, beheld his never-to-be-forgotten Mary Brand; whilst she, hardly believing her senses, recognised in her deliverer her former lover, and still well-beloved La Bonté.

"What, Mary! can it be you?" he asked, looking intently upon the trembling woman.

"La Bonté, you don't forget me!" she answered, and threw herself sobbing into the arms of the sturdy mountaineer.

There we will leave her for the present, and help Killbuck and his companions to examine the killed

U

and wounded. Of the former, five Indians and two whites lay dead, grandchildren of old Brand, fine lads of fourteen or fifteen, who had fought with the greatest bravery, and lay pierced with arrows and lance wounds. Old Brand had received a sore buffet, but a hatful of cold water from the creek sprinkled over his face soon restored him. His sons had not escaped scot-free, and Antoine was shot through the neck, and, falling, had actually been half scalped by an Indian, whom the timely arrival of La Bonté had caused to leave his work unfinished.

Silently, and with sad hearts, the survivors of the family saw the bodies of the two boys buried on the river bank, and the spot marked with a pile of loose stones, procured from the rocky bed of the creek. The carcasses of the treacherous Indians were left to be devoured by wolves, and their bones to bleach in the sun and wind—a warning to their tribe, that such foul treachery as they had meditated had met with a merited retribution.

The next day the party continued their course to the Platte. Antoine and the stranger returned to the Arkansa, starting in the night to avoid the Indians; but Killbuck and La Bonté lent the aid of their rifles to the solitary caravan, and, under their experienced guidance, no more Indian perils were encountered. Mary no longer sat perched up in her father's Conostoga, but rode a quiet mustang by La Bonté's side; and no doubt they found a theme with which to while away the monotonous journey over the dreary plains. South Fork was passed, and Laramie was reached. The Sweet Water mountains, which hang over the " pass " to California, were long since in sight; but when the waters of the North Fork of Platte lay before their horses' feet, and the broad trail was pointed out which led to the great valley of Columbia and their promised land, the heads of the oxen were turned *down* the stream where the shallow waters flow on to join the great Missouri—and not *up*, towards the mountains where they leave their spring-heads, from which springs flow several waters—some coursing their way to the eastward, fertilising, in their route to the Atlantic, the lands of civilised man ; others westward, forcing a passage through rocky cañons, and flowing through a barren wilderness, inhabited by fierce and barbarous tribes.

These were the routes to choose from : and, whatever was the cause, the oxen turned their yoked heads away from the rugged mountains ; the teamsters joyfully cracked their ponderous whips, as the waggons rolled lightly down the Platte ; and men, women, and children, waved their hats and bonnets in the air, and cried out lustily, " Hurrah for home ! "

La Bonté looked at the dark sombre mountains ere he turned his back upon them for the last time. He thought of the many years he had spent beneath their rugged shadow, of the many hardships he had suffered, of all his pains and perils in those wild re-

gions. The most exciting episodes of his adventurous
career, his tried companions in scenes of fierce fight
and bloodshed, passed in review before him. A
feeling of regret was creeping over him, when Mary
laid her hand gently on his shoulder. One single
tear rolled unbidden down his cheek, and he answered her inquiring eyes : " I'm not sorry to leave
it, Mary, " he said ; " but it's hard to turn one's
back upon old friends."

They had a hard battle with Killbuck, in endeavouring to persuade him to accompany them to the
settlements. The old mountaineer shook his head.
" The time, " he said " was gone by for that. He
had often thought of it, but, when the day arrived,
he hadn't heart to leave the mountains. Trapping
now was of no account, he knew ; but beaver was
bound to rise, and then the good times would come
again. What could he do in the settlements, where
there wasn't room to move, and where it was hard
to breathe—there were so many people ? "

He accompanied them a considerable distance
down the river, ever and anon looking cautiously
back, to ascertain that he had not gone out of sight
of the mountains. Before reaching the forks, however, he finally bade them adieu ; and, turning the
head of his old grizzled mule westward, he heartily
wrung the hand of his comrade La Bonté ; and,
crying Yep ! to his well-tried animal, disappeared
behind a roll of the prairie, and was seen no more

—a thousand good wishes for the welfare of the sturdy trapper speeding him on his solitary way.

Four months from the day when La Bonté so opportunely appeared to rescue Brand's family from the Indians on Black Horse Creek, that worthy and the faithful Mary were duly and lawfully united in the township church of Brandville, Memphis county, State of Tennessee. We cannot say, in the concluding words of nine hundred and ninety-nine thousand novels, that "numerous pledges of mutual love surrounded and cheered them in their declining years," &c. &c.; because it was only on the 24th of July, in the year of our Lord 1847, that La Bonté and Mary Brand were finally made one, after fifteen long years of separation.

The fate of one of the humble characters who have figured in these pages, we must yet tarry a little longer to describe.

During the past winter, a party of mountaineers, flying from overpowering numbers of hostile Sioux, found themselves, one stormy evening, in a wild and dismal cañon near the elevated mountain valley called the "New Park."

The rocky bed of a dry mountain torrent, whose waters were now locked up at their spring-heads by icy fetters, was the only road up which they could

make their difficult way : for the rugged sides of
the gorge rose precipitously from the creek, scarcely affording a foot-hold to even the active bighorn,
which occasionally looked down upon the travellers
from the lofty summit. Logs of pine, uprooted by the
hurricanes which sweep incessantly through the
mountain defiles, and tossed headlong from the surrounding ridges, continually obstructed their way ;
and huge rocks and boulders, fallen from the
heights and blocking up the bed of the stream, added to the difficulty, and threatened them every
instant with destruction.

Towards sundown they reached a point where
the cañon opened out into a little shelving glade or
prairie, a few hundred yards in extent, the entrance
to which was almost hidden by a thicket of dwarf
pine and cedar. Here they determined to encamp
for the night, in a spot secure from Indians, and, as
they imagined, untrodden by the foot of man.

What, however, was their astonishment, on breaking through the cedar-covered entrance, to perceive
a solitary horse standing motionless in the centre of
the prairie. Drawing near, they found it to be an
old grizzled mustang, or Indian pony, with cropped
ears and ragged tail, (well picked by hungry mules),
standing doubled up with cold, and at the very last
gasp from extreme old age and weakness. Its bones
were nearly through the stiffened skin, the legs of
the animal were gathered under it ; whilst its for-
lorn-looking head and stretched-out neck hung

listlessly downwards, almost overbalancing its tottering body. The glazed and sunken eye—the protruding and froth-covered tongue—the heaving flank and quivering tail—declared its race was run; and the driving sleet and snow, and penetrating winter blast, scarce made impression upon its callous and worn-out frame.

One of the band of mountaineers was Marcellin, and a single look at the miserable beast was sufficient for him to recognise the once renowned Nezpercé steed of old Bill Williams. That the owner himself was not far distant he felt certain; and, searching carefully around, the hunters presently came upon an old camp, before which lay, protruding from the snow, the blackened remains of pine logs. Before these, which had been the fire, and leaning with his back against a pine trunk, and his legs crossed under him, half covered with snow, reclined the figure of the old mountaineer, his snow-capped head bent over his breast. His well-known hunting-coat of fringed elk-skin hung stiff and weather-stained about him; and his rifle, packs, and traps, were strewed around.

Awe-struck, the trappers approached the body, and found it frozen hard as stone, in which state it had probably lain there for many days or weeks. A jagged rent in the breast of his leather coat, and dark stains about it, showed he had received a wound before his death; but it was impossible to say, whether to his hurt, or to sickness, or to the natural decay of age, was to be attributed the wretched and solitary end of poor Bill Williams.

A friendly bullet cut short the few remaining hours of the trapper's faithful steed; and burying, as well as they were able, the body of the old mountaineer, the hunters next day left him in his lonely grave, in a spot so wild and remote, that it was doubtful whether even hungry wolves would discover and disinter his attenuated corpse.

THE END.

PRINTED BY JOHN HUGHES, 3 THISTLE STREET, EDINBURGH.